New York State Coach
March-to-March Edition
Mathematics
Grade 8

Coach™
America's Best for Student Success®

Triumph Learning®

A Haights Cross Communications ® Company

New York State Coach, March-to-March Edition, Mathematics, Grade 8
128NY
ISBN-10: 1-59823-458-7
ISBN-13: 978-1-59823-458-9

Cover Image: Eduoard Berne/Getty Images

Triumph Learning® 136 Madison Avenue, 7th Floor, New York, NY 10016
Kevin McAliley, President and Chief Executive Officer

Table of Contents

GRADE 7 POST-MARCH LESSONS

NY State Grade 7 Post-March Indicators

7.A.3
7.A.2
7.A.4
7.A.7, 7.A.8
7.A.9, 7.A.10

7.G.5, 7.G.6, 7.G.8
7.G.9

7.M.1
7.M.5, 7.M.6
7.M.7

GRADE 8 PRE-MARCH LESSONS

NY State Grade 8 Pre-March Indicators

8.N.1, 8.N.2
8.N.3
8.N.4
8.N.5, 8.N.6

To the Student

This book will help you get ready for the Grade 8 New York State Math Test.

The *New York State Coach, March-to-March Edition, Mathematics Grade 8* is divided into three parts. The first part is called **Grade 7 Post-March Lessons**. These lessons are part of Grade 7, but were taught *after* the March Test *last year*. The second part is the **Grade 8 Pre-March Lessons**. These two parts have all the content you need to get ready for the New York State Grade 8 Math Test.

The third part is called **Grade 8 Post-March Lessons**. These lessons, which are taught *after* the March Test *this year*, cover mathematics not tested on the Grade 8 Test. With the Post-March lessons, this Coach covers all Grade 8 Indicators. The names Pre-March and Post-March come from the month when math tests are given.

The main parts of the lessons are Examples. Examples begin with math questions similar to test questions and explain step by step how to find answers to the questions.

You will practice three types of questions just like the ones on the test. One type is the Multiple-Choice Question (MCQ). After each MCQ there are four answers. Only one is correct. Choose the one answer that is correct.

The test also has a number of questions that have two parts. These are called Short-Response Questions (SRQ). The first part of a SRQ asks for a short answer. The second part asks for an explanation of how you got the answer to the first part.

The third type of question is like the SRQ, except longer. This third type is called Extended-Response Question (ERQ). The word "extended" tells us that it is like the SRQ, but longer. Each ERQ is made up of several linked parts. One part of the ERQ asks you to write a full answer to that part. Other parts may ask you to draw a diagram or give a full explanation of your solution to the question.

This book has many features that will help you: Examples in all lessons; an interactive Check It Out with the Coach in every lesson; and Progress Checks at the end of each section. A Glossary at the end of the book helps with special vocabulary and explains many concepts. When you finish this book, you will be ready for the New York State Math Test.

This table shows you the schedule for the New York State Grade 8 Math Test.

Day 1 Session 1	27 multiple-choice questions	50 minutes, plus an additional 10 minutes prep time
Session 2	4 short-response questions and 2 extended-response questions	40 minutes, plus an additional 10 minutes prep time
Day 2 Session 3	8 short-response questions and 4 extended-response questions	70 minutes, plus an additional 10 minutes prep time

Correlation Chart of New York State Grade 7 Post-March and Grade 8 Pre- and Post-March Math Indicators to *Coach* Lessons

NEW YORK STATE GRADE 7 MATH INDICATORS (Post-March)		COACH LESSON
STRAND 2: ALGEBRA		
Variables and Expressions: *Students will represent and analyze algebraically a wide variety of problem solving situations.*		
7.A.2	Add and subtract monomials with exponents of one	2
7.A.3	Identify a polynomial as an algebraic expression containing one or more terms	1
Equations and Inequalities: *Students will perform algebraic procedures accurately.*		
7.A.4	Solve multi-step equations by combining like terms, using the distributive property, or moving variables to one side of the equation	3
Patterns, Relations and Functions: *Students will recognize, use, and represent algebraically patterns, relations, and functions.*		
7.A.7	Draw the graphic representation of a pattern from an equation or from a table of data	4
7.A.8	Create algebraic patterns using charts/tables, graphs, equations, and expressions	4
7.A.9	Build a pattern to develop a rule for determining the sum of the interior angles of polygons	5
7.A.10	Write an equation to represent a function from a table of values	5
STRAND 3: GEOMETRY		
Geometric Relationships: *Students will identify and justify geometric relationships, formally and informally.*		
7.G.5	Identify the right angle, hypotenuse, and legs of a right triangle	6
7.G.6	Explore the relationship between the lengths of the three sides of a right triangle to develop the Pythagorean Theorem	6
7.G.8	Use the Pythagorean Theorem to determine the unknown length of a side of a right triangle	6
7.G.9	Determine whether a given triangle is a right triangle by applying the Pythagorean Theorem and using a calculator	7
STRAND 4: MEASUREMENT		
Units of Measurement: *Students will determine what can be measured and how, using appropriate methods and formulas.*		
7.M.1	Calculate distance using a map scale	8
7.M.5	Calculate unit price using proportions	9
7.M.6	Compare unit prices	9
7.M.7	Convert money between different currencies with the use of an exchange rate table and a calculator	10

NEW YORK STATE GRADE 8 MATH INDICATORS (Pre-March)		COACH LESSON
STRAND 1: NUMBER SENSE AND OPERATIONS		
Operations: *Students will understand meanings of operations and procedures, and how they relate to one another.*		
8.N.1	Develop and apply the laws of exponents for multiplication and division	11
8.N.2	Evaluate expressions with integral exponents	11
8.N.3	Read, write, and identify percents less than 1% and greater than 100%	12
8.N.4	Apply percents to: Tax, percent increase/decrease, simple interest, sale price, commission, interest rates, and gratuities	13
Estimation: *Students will compute accurately and make reasonable estimates.*		
8.N.5	Estimate a percent of quantity, given an application	14
8.N.6	Justify the reasonableness of answers using estimation	14
STRAND 2: ALGEBRA		
Variables and Expressions: *Students will represent and analyze algebraically a wide variety of problem solving situations*		
8.A.1	Translate verbal sentences into algebraic inequalities	16
8.A.2	Write verbal expressions that match given mathematical expressions	15
8.A.3	Describe a situation involving relationships that matches a given graph	17
8.A.4	Create a graph given a description or an expression for a situation involving a linear or nonlinear relationship	17
8.A.5	Use physical models to perform operations with polynomials	PC15–23 OEQ
Variables and Expressions: *Students will perform algebraic procedures accurately.*		
8.A.6	Multiply and divide monomials	19
8.A.7	Add and subtract polynomials (integer coefficients)	18
8.A.8	Multiply a binomial by a monomial or a binomial (integer coefficients)	20
8.A.9	Divide a polynomial by a monomial (integer coefficients) *Note: The degree of the denominator is less than or equal to the degree of the numerator for all variables.*	19
8.A.10	Factor algebraic expressions using the GCF	21
8.A.11	Factor a trinomial in the form $ax^2 + bx + c$; $a = 1$ and c having no more than three sets of factors	22
Equations and Inequalities		
8.A.12	Apply algebra to determine the measure of angles formed by or contained in parallel lines cut by a transversal and by intersecting lines	PC24–27 OEQ

NEW YORK STATE GRADE 8 MATH INDICATORS (Pre-March)	COACH LESSON
Patterns, Relations, and Functions: *Students will recognize, use, and represent algebraically patterns, relations, and functions.*	
8.A.15 Understand that numerical information can be represented in multiple ways: arithmetically, algebraically, and graphically	23
8.A.16 Find a set of ordered pairs to satisfy a given linear numerical pattern (expressed algebraically); then plot the ordered pairs and draw the line	17
STRAND 3: GEOMETRY	
Geometric Relationships: *Students will identify and justify geometric relationships, formally and informally.*	
8.G.1 Identify pairs of vertical angles as congruent	24
8.G.2 Identify pairs of supplementary and complementary angles	24
8.G.3 Calculate the missing angle in a supplementary or complementary pair	24
8.G.4 Determine angle pair relationships when given two parallel lines cut by a transversal	25
8.G.5 Calculate the missing angle measurements when given two parallel lines cut by a transversal	25
8.G.6 Calculate the missing angle measurements when given two intersecting lines and an angle	24
Transformational Geometry: *Students will apply transformations and symmetry to analyze problem solving situations.*	
8.G.7 Describe and identify transformations in the plane, using proper function notation (rotations, reflections, translations, and dilations)	26, 27
8.G.8 Draw the image of a figure under rotations of 90 and 180 degrees	26
8.G.9 Draw the image of a figure under a reflection over a given line	26
8.G.10 Draw the image of a figure under a translation	26
8.G.11 Draw the image of a figure under a dilation	27
8.G.12 Identify the properties preserved and not preserved under a reflection, rotation, translation, and dilation	26, 27
STRAND 4: MEASUREMENT	
Units of Measurement: *Students will determine what can be measured and how, using appropriate methods and formulas.*	
8.M.1 Solve equations/proportions to convert to equivalent measurements within metric and customary measurement systems. Note: also allow Fahrenheit to Celsius and vice versa	28

NEW YORK STATE GRADE 8 MATH INDICATORS (Post-March)	COACH LESSON
STRAND 2: ALGEBRA	
Equations and Inequalities	
8.A.13 Solve multi-step inequalities and graph the solution set on a number line	29
8.A.14 Solve linear inequalities by combining like terms, using the distributive property, or moving variables to one side of the inequality (include multiplication or division of inequalities by a negative number)	29
Patterns, Relations, and Functions: *Students will recognize, use, and represent algebraically patterns, relations, and functions.*	
8.A.17 Define and use correct terminology when referring to function (domain and range)	30
8.A.18 Determine if a relation is a function	30
8.A.19 Interpret multiple representations using equation, table of values, and graph	31
STRAND 3: GEOMETRY	
Constructions: *Students will use visualization and spatial reasoning to analyze characteristics and properties of geometric shapes.*	
8.G.0 Construct the following using a straight edge and compass: segment congruent to a segment, angle congruent to an angle, perpendicular bisector, angle bisector	32
Coordinate Geometry: *Students will apply coordinate geometry to analyze problem solving situations.*	
8.G.13 Determine the slope of a line from a graph and explain the meaning of slope as a constant rate of change	33
8.G.14 Determine the y-intercept of a line from a graph and be able to explain the y-intercept	34
8.G.15 Graph a line using a table of values	34
8.G.16 Determine the equation of a line given the slope and the y-intercept	35
8.G.17 Graph a line from an equation in slope-intercept form ($y = mx + b$)	35
8.G.18 Solve systems of equations graphically (only linear, integral solutions, $y = mx + b$ format, no vertical/horizontal lines)	37
8.G.19 Graph the solution set of an inequality on a number line	29
8.G.20 Distinguish between linear and nonlinear equations $ax^2 + bx + c; a = 1$ (only graphically)	36
8.G.21 Recognize the characteristics of quadratics in tables, equations, and situations	38

Competencies Analysis Chart and *Coach* Lesson Correlation for Practice Tests 1 and 2

Practice Test Question	Standards and Indicators				Coach Lessons
	N	**A**	**G**	**M**	
SESSION 1					
Multiple Choice					
1	8.N.2				11
2		8.A.2			15
3	8.N.1				11
4	8.N.4				13
5		7.A.4			3
6			7.G.5		6
7				8.M.1	28
8	8.N.3				12
9			7.G.8		4
10		8.A.1			16
11	8.N.5				13
12			8.G.2, 8.G.3		24
13		8.A.6			19
14			8.G.7		26, 27
15	8.N.6				14
16		8.A.6, 8.A.8			19, 20
17		8.A.12	8.G.5		PC24–27 OEQ, 25
18		7.A.2			2
19		7.A.7			4
20		8.A.3			17
21		8.A.6, 8.A.9			19
22			8.G.1, 8.G.6		24
23		8.A.11			22
24			7.G.9		7
25				7.M.1	8
26				7.M.6	9
27		8.A.7			18
SESSION 2					
Short Response					
28	8.N.4				13
29		8.A.10			21
30		7.A.10			5
31				8.M.1	28
Extended Response					
32			8.G.9, 8.G.10, 8.G.12		26, 27
33		8.A.11			22
SESSION 3					
Short Response					
34	8.N.1				11
35		8.A.16			17
36	8.N.5				14
37				7.M.7	10
38	8.N.2				11
39				8.M.1	28
40		8.A.5			PC15–23 OEQ
41	8.N.6				14
Extended Response					
42			8.G.1, 8.G.2, 8.G.3, 8.G.6		24
43				7.M.5, 7.M.6	9
44			8.G.11, 8.G.12		26, 27
45			8.G.7, 8.G.12		26, 27

Practice Test 1

Session 1

1 What is the value of y^{-3} when $y = 2$?

A $-\frac{1}{6}$ C $\frac{1}{8}$

B $-\frac{1}{8}$ D $\frac{1}{6}$

2 The variable s stands for the number of units in the side of a square. Which verbal expression matches this expression?

$4s + 4$

F the perimeter of the square increased by 4 units

G the perimeter of the square decreased by 4 units

H four times the perimeter of the square increased by 4 units

J the product of 4 and the perimeter of the square

3 $(4^2)^3 = $ _____

A 4^1 C 4^6

B 4^5 D 4^8

4 A restaurant automatically adds a tip of 18% to checks for groups of 6 or more people. Jessica and 5 of her friends went to the restaurant. The bill before tip came to $135. How much will the restaurant add to the bill as a tip?

F $18.60

G $20.80

H $23.50

J $24.30

5 Solve the equation $4(x - 3) + 7 = 23$ for x.

A $x = 1$

B $x = 7$

C $x = 87$

D $x = 123$

6 In the triangle below, which is the hypotenuse?

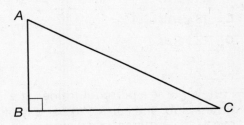

F $\overline{AB}$

G $\overline{BC}$

H $\overline{AC}$

J $\angle ABC$

7 The average normal temperature in Albany in May is about 59°F. What is this temperature in degrees Celsius?

A 5°C

B 15°C

C 25°C

D 35°C

Go On

8 Chandler is part of a team that wrote a high school math book. He receives a $\frac{5}{8}$% royalty of the sales of the book. Which of the following is equivalent to $\frac{5}{8}$%?

F   0.000625

G   0.00625

H   0.0625

J   0.625

9 The hypotenuse of a right triangle is 39 yards. One leg of the triangle is 15 yards. What is the length of the other leg of the triangle?

A   36 yards

B   24 yards

C   18 yards

D   12 yards

10 Priti works as a personal trainer at a fitness club. She earns $50 per day plus $30 for each fitness club member she trains. She wants to make at least $200 today. Which inequality can be used to find m, the number of fitness club members she will have to train?

F $30m - 50 \geq 200$

G $50m + 30 \geq 200$

H $30m + 50 \geq 200$

J $30m + 50 < 200$

11 Sondra has $1,980 to invest. What is the **best** estimate of the amount of simple interest she can earn if she invests the money for 2 years at a rate of 4.5%?

A $100

B $200

C $300

D $400

12 Lines AB and CD intersect at point E. Ray EF is perpendicular to line AB.

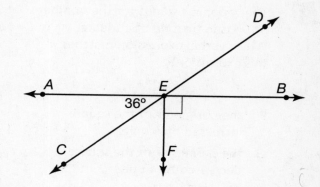

What is the measure of $\angle CEF$?

F   36°

G   44°

H   54°

J   64°

13 $\dfrac{100c^6}{-25c^4} = $ _____

A $-2{,}500c^{10}$

B $-2{,}500c^2$

C $-4c^{10}$

D $-4c^2$

14 △A′B′C′ is the image of △ABC after a transformation.

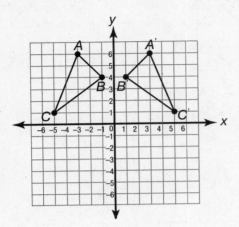

What was the transformation?

F a reflection over the x-axis

G a reflection over the y-axis

H a translation of 6 units to the right

J a dilation with scale factor 2

15 Last year, the population of the town where Jared lives increased from 21,900 to 22,020. Using a calculator, he computed the percent increase to the nearest whole percent to be 5%. Use estimation to choose the correct statement.

A His calculation is correct.

B His calculation is about $4\frac{1}{2}$ percentage points too high.

C His calculation is about $4\frac{1}{2}$ percentage points too low.

D His calculation is about 10 percentage points too high.

16 $(4x + 3)(3x - 2) =$

F $12x^2 + x - 6$

G $12x^2 - x - 6$

H $12x^2 - x + 6$

J $12x^2 + 17x - 6$

17 Lines a and b are parallel, and line t is a transversal. If $m\angle 1 = (2x + 7)°$ and $m\angle 2 = (3x + 3)°$, what is the measure of $\angle 1$?

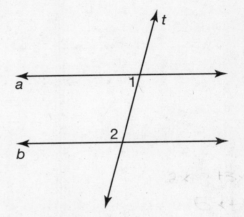

A 34°   **C** 75°

B 68°   **D** 85°

18 Simplify the expression.

$$18h - 12 - 9h + 32$$

F $9h + 20$

G $9h - 20$

H $27h + 20$

J $27h - 20$

Go On

19 Which graph matches this table?

x	y
−2	4
−1	2
0	0
1	2
2	4

A

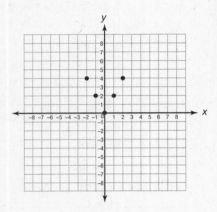

C

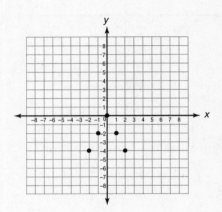

B

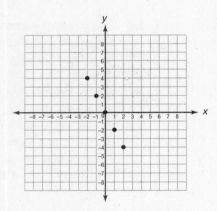

D

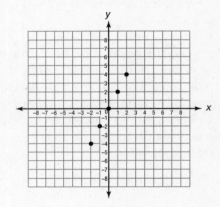

20 Hank drove to visit his cousin who lives 150 miles away. He began driving at 4:00 P.M. This graph shows his progress during the trip.

During which of the following time periods was he traveling at the greatest average speed?

F between 4:00 P.M. and 5:00 P.M.

G between 5:00 P.M. and 7:00 P.M.

H between 7:00 P.M. and 8:00 P.M.

J between 8:00 P.M. and 9:00 P.M.

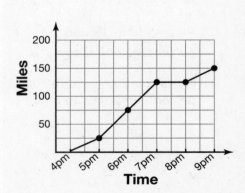

Go On

Test 1: Session 1

21 $\dfrac{18x^4 + 24x^3 - 6x^2}{6x^2} = $ _____

  A $3x^2 + 4x$

  B $3x^2 + 4x - 1$

  C $3x^2 + 4x - 6$

  D $3x^6 + 4x^5 - 1x^4$

22 Lines *RS* and *TV* intersect at point *O*.

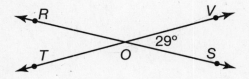

Which statement is true?

  F m∠*TOR* = 29°, m∠*ROV* = 151°,
     m∠*TOS* = 151°

  G m∠*TOR* = 29°, m∠*ROV* = 151°,
     m∠*TOS* = 29°

  H m∠*TOR* = 29°, m∠*ROV* = 29°,
     m∠*TOS* = 151°

  J m∠*TOR* = 151°, m∠*ROV* = 29°,
     m∠*TOS* = 29°

23 What is $n^2 + 7n + 12$ in factored form?

  A $(n + 2)(n + 6)$

  B $(n + 6)(n + 6)$

  C $(n + 3)(n + 4)$

  D $(n + 1)(n + 12)$

24 Which set of dimensions below will form a right triangle?

  F 10 cm, 30 cm, 40 cm

  G 10 cm, 12 cm, 16 cm

  H 10 cm, 25 cm, 30 cm

  J 10 cm, 24 cm, 26 cm

25 The distance between two cities on a map is $3\frac{1}{2}$ inches. The scale of the map is $\frac{1}{2}$ in. = 5 miles. What is the actual distance between the cities?

  A 15 miles

  B 30 miles

  C 35 miles

  D 45 miles

26 It costs \$15.00 to buy 150 sheets of Brand A paper. It costs \$19.25 to buy 175 sheets of Brand B paper. Which brand has the better value and by how much?

  F Brand A: 1 cent

  G Brand A: 2 cents

  H Brand B: 1 cent

  J Brand B: 2 cents

27 The Wilson family wants to rent a storage room for some of their furniture. The storage facility has two room sizes available. The floor area of the larger storage room is represented by the polynomial $3x^2 + x - 2$, and the floor area of the smaller room is represented by the polynomial $x^2 + 2x + 1$. Which polynomial represents the greater size of the larger room?

  A $2x^4 - x^2 - 3$

  B $2x^2 + 3x - 1$

  C $2x^2 - x - 3$

  D $3x^2 - 2x - 3$

STOP

Session 2

28   A clothing store purchased jackets for $40 each and put them on sale for $70. What was the percent markup on each jacket?

Show your work.

Answer _____ %

29   Study the terms in this trinomial.

$$28x^3 - 14x^2 + 7x$$

Part A

Write the polynomial as the product of the GCF of all its terms and a polynomial.

Answer _____

Part B

Explain how you determined your answer to Part A.

_____

_____

_____

_____

_____

Go On

30   Look at the function table.

x	y
0	−15
1	−7
2	1
3	9
4	17
5	25

Part A

Write the equation that shows how to determine the value of *y* for any value of *x*.

Answer _____

Part B

Use the equation to find the corresponding *y*-values for x = 6, 7, and 8.

Answer _____

31   The interior dimensions of a carton in the shape of a rectangular prism are 2 ft by 1 ft by $1\frac{1}{2}$ ft.

Part A

How many boxes, each in the shape of a cube with 1-inch edges, will fit inside the carton?
Show your work.

Answer _____

Part B

Explain your steps for finding the answer to Part A.

_____

_____

_____

_____

_____

Go On

32   △*RST* is graphed on
the coordinate grid below.

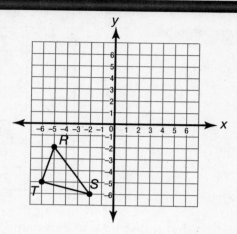

Part A

On the coordinate grid above, graph △*R'S'T'*, the image of △*RST* after a translation of
8 units to the right.

Part B

How do the size and shape of △*R'S'T'* compare with the size and shape of △*RST*?

Answer _____

Part C

On the coordinate grid above, graph △*R"S"T"*, the image of △*R'S'T'* after a reflection
over the *x*-axis.

Part D

How did you determine the coordinates of the vertices of △*R"S"T"*?

Answer _____

33   Look at the trinomial below.

$x^2 + 8x + 15$

Part A

Factor the trinomial as the product of two binomials.

Answer _____

Part B

Use what you know about binomials and trinomials to explain how you found your answer
to Part A.

_____

Part C

Suppose the middle term of the trinomial had been −8*x* instead of 8*x*. How would the
factored form change?

_____

STOP

Test 1: Session 2

Session 3

34 $3^4 \times 3^3 = 3^n$

What is the value of *n* in the equation above?

Show your work.

Answer _____

35 This is a linear equation.

$y = \frac{1}{2}x + 1$

Part A

Complete this table of values for the equation.

x	y
−4	
−2	
0	
2	
4	

Part B

Use the values from the table in Part A to graph the equation at right.

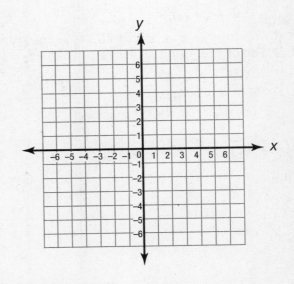

Go On

36 A 1995 model of a computer that originally sold for $2,998 is now selling at 31% of its original selling price. Estimate the selling price of the computer now.

Show your work.

Answer _____

37 During her trip to Europe, Mary learned that 1 euro was equivalent to the value of 1.28 U.S. dollars.

Part A

Mary began her trip with $2,000 U.S. dollars. How many euros did Mary have?
Show your work.

Answer _____ euros

Part B

After her trip, Mary had 740 euros left. What was the value in U.S. dollars?
Show your work.

Answer $_____

Go On

Test 1: Session 3

38 Joan used the digits 2, 3, 4, and 5 to form this expression.

$5^2 \times 3^4$

What is the value of Joan's expression?

Show your work.

Answer _____

39 Harold wants to cover the floors of his home with carpeting. He has 1,728 square feet of floor to cover.

Part A

Write a proportion to find n, the number of square yards of carpet he needs to buy.

Proportion _____

Part B

Solve your proportion to find how many square yards of carpeting Harold needs to buy.

Show your work.

Answer _____ square yards

Go On

40 This rectangle is the model for the product of two binomials. In the model, each small square represents 1, each rectangle represents x, and the large square represents x^2.

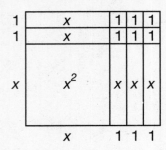

The area of the rectangle is the product of the length and the width. The length of the rectangle above is $x + 3$ and the width is $x + 2$. The rectangle is made up of 1 large square plus 5 rectangles plus 6 small squares, which is $x^2 + 5x + 6$, the product you would get if you multiplied the binomials $x + 3$ and $x + 2$.

What two binomials would give the product shown in the model below?

Show your work.

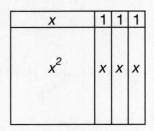

Answer _____

41 Keith's family is booking a hotel suite for a weekend. The regular price of the suite is $392. They have a coupon for a 25% discount. Keith used his calculator to find the amount of discount and got $9.80.

Part A

How can you use estimation to check the reasonableness of Keith's calculation?

_____

Part B

Without doing the calculation, tell whether or not Keith's calculator result is reasonable. Explain your answer.

_____

_____

Go On

42   Lines *m* and *n* intersect to form angles 1, 2, 3, and 4. The measure of ∠1 is 36°.

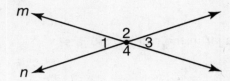

Part A

What is the measure of ∠3?

Answer _____

Part B

Explain why your answer to Part A is correct.

_____

_____

_____

_____

Part C

What is the measure of ∠2?

Answer _____

Part D

Explain why your answer to Part C is correct.

_____

_____

_____

_____

Go On

43 It costs $350 for a case of 150 jars of modeling clay. It costs $672 for a case of 450 jars of modeling clay.

Part A

What is the unit price for a jar in the case of 150 jars?
Show your work.

Answer $_____

Part B

What is the unit price for a jar in the case of 450 jars?
Show your work.

Answer $_____

Part C

Which case of jars of modeling clay is the better buy?

Answer _____

Go On

44 △*PQR* is graphed below.

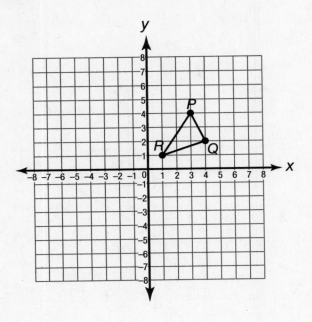

Part A

On the coordinate grid above, graph △*P'Q'R'*, the image of △*PQR*, after a dilation with a scale factor of 2.

Part B

How do the size and shape of △*P'Q'R'* compare with the size and shape of △*PQR*?

_____

_____

Part C

Explain your answer to Part B.

_____

_____

_____

_____

_____

Go On

Test 1: Session 3

45 Figure 1 and Figure 2 are graphed below.

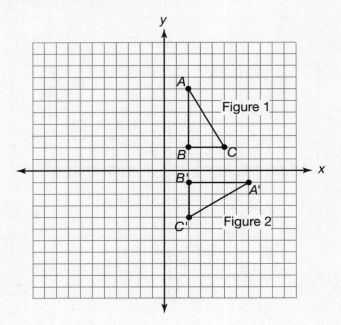

Part A

Explain how Figure 1 was transformed to Figure 2.

_____

_____

_____

_____

Part B

Are Figure 1 and Figure 2 congruent? Explain.

_____

_____

_____

_____

STOP

Test 1: Session 3

FORMULAS	CONVERSIONS
Pythagorean Theorem	Temperature Conversion $F = \frac{9}{5}C + 32$ $C = \frac{5}{9}(F - 32)$
Simple Interest $\quad I = prt$	
Distance Formula $\quad d = rt$	Measurement Conversions 1 mile = 5,280 feet 1 yard = 3 feet
Slope-Intercept Formula $\quad y = mx + b$ m = slope b = y-intercept	

LESSON

1

Strand 2: Algebra

Polynomials

7.A.3 Identify a polynomial as an algebraic expression containing one or more terms

MONOMIALS

A **monomial** is a single variable or number, or a product of a number and one or more variables, with exponents that are whole numbers.

NOTE: A monomial cannot have a variable in the denominator.

These expressions are monomials: $7x$ -32 $14y^2$ z $6xy$

These expressions are not monomials: $\dfrac{3x}{y}$ $\dfrac{5}{b^2}$

If a monomial is the product of a number and one or more variables, the number in front of the variable is the **coefficient** of the variable or variables.

> For example, for $6xy$, 6 is the coefficient of xy; and for $14y^2$, 14 is the coefficient of y^2.
> For the monomial z, 1 is the coefficient of z because $z = 1z$.

If a number stands alone, it is a **monomial constant**, or simply a constant. -32 by itself is a constant. So is -23 in the expression $14x^4 - 7x - 23$.

POLYNOMIALS

A **polynomial** is a monomial or the sum or difference of monomials.

These expressions are polynomials: $3y$ $4x + 2y - 3z$ $12x^2 + 2y^3$

BINOMIALS

If two monomials are added or subtracted, they form a **binomial**, which is a type of polynomial.

These expressions are binomials: $3xy - 17$ $5y^3 - 20$ $x + y$

Each monomial is a **term** of the binomial, so a binomial is made up of two terms.

TRINOMIALS

If three monomials are added or subtracted, they form a **trinomial**, which is a type of polynomial.

These expressions are trinomials: $5x + y - 17$ $2y^2 + 3y + 8$ $x^3 - x + 1$

Each monomial is a term of the trinomial, so a trinomial is made up of three terms.

EXAMPLE 1

What type of expression is $3x^2 + 9x - 5$?

A   A monomial

B   A binomial

C   A trinomial

D   A coefficient

STRATEGY

Count the number of terms in the expression.

> There are 3 terms.
>
> A trinomial has 3 terms, so the expression is a trinomial.

SOLUTION

The expression $3x^2 + 9x - 5$ is a trinomial.

EXAMPLE 2

Which expression is a polynomial?

$\frac{2x}{8y}$, $8x$, $\frac{9xy}{y^5}$, $8x^{0.5}$

STRATEGY

Use the definition of a polynomial.

> $\frac{2x}{8y}$ is not a polynomial because there is a variable in the denominator.
>
> $8x$ is a polynomial because it is a product of a number and a variable.
>
> $\frac{9xy}{y^5}$ is not a polynomial because there is a variable in the denominator.
>
> $8x^{0.5}$ is not a polynomial because the exponent 0.5 is not a whole number.

SOLUTION

The expression $8x$ is a polynomial.

What type of expression is $9y^5 + 45$?

Let's check it out.

How many terms are in the expression? _____

What is the name of the polynomial that has 2 terms? _____

So the expression $9y^5 + 45$ is a _____.

Sample Test Questions

1 What type of expression is $16 - x$?

   A A trinomial

   B A coefficient

   C A binomial

   D A monomial

2 What type of expression is $2 - x + x^2$?

   F A trinomial

   G A coefficient

   H A binomial

   J A monomial

3 How many terms are in a monomial?

   A 0

   B 1

   C 2

   D 3

4 How many terms are in a trinomial?

   F 0

   G 1

   H 2

   J 3

5 Which of these is a monomial?

   A $x - 1$

   B 65

   C $14 - x + y$

   D $\frac{3}{x^3}$

6 Which of these is a trinomial?

   F 2

   G $5x - \frac{4x}{y^2}$

   H $10 + 3y^2 - xy$

   J $6 - x$

7 What type of expression is $-34xyz^3$?

   A A monomial

   B A binomial

   C A trinomial

   D A term

8 What type of expression is $0.94 + z^4$?

   F A monomial

   G A binomial

   H A trinomial

   J A term

9 What describes the number -4 in $-4xyz$?

   Answer _____

10 What describes 64 in $64 - y^2$?

   Answer _____

Short-Response Question

11 Mrs. Potter wrote the expression $7x^2 + 3x$ on the chalkboard.

Part A

What type of expression did Mrs. Potter write on the chalkboard?

Answer _____

Part B

Use what you know about polynomials to explain why your answer is correct. Use words and/or numbers to support your explanation.

_____

_____

_____

_____

LESSON 2

Strand 2: Algebra

Adding and Subtracting Monomials

7.A.2 Add and subtract monomials with exponents of one

Some expressions contain like terms. **Like terms** have the same variables raised to the same power. Here are some examples:

$5x$ and $-3x$, $4b$ and $10b$, $2x^2$ and $\frac{1}{2}x^2$, y^4 and $9y^4$

EXAMPLE 1

Simplify this expression by combining like terms.

$9a + 15a$

STRATEGY

Use the distributive property.

STEP 1 Use the distributive property to write the sum as a product.

$9a + 15a = a(9 + 15)$

STEP 2 Do the operation in parentheses.

$a(9 + 15) = a \times 24$

STEP 3 Use the commutative property of multiplication.

$a \times 24 = 24 \times a = 24a$

SOLUTION

$9a + 15a = 24a$

EXAMPLE 2

Simplify this expression by combining like terms.

$\frac{1}{4}z + 8 + \frac{3}{4}z - 5$

STRATEGY

Use the commutative property of addition and then the distributive property.

STEP 1 Use the commutative property of addition to rearrange the terms.

$\frac{1}{4}z + 8 + \frac{3}{4}z - 5 = \frac{1}{4}z + \frac{3}{4}z + 8 - 5$

STEP 2 Combine the terms with variables.

$\frac{1}{4}z + \frac{3}{4}z + 8 - 5$

$z(\frac{1}{4} + \frac{3}{4}) + 8 - 5$

$z(1) + 8 - 5$

$1z + 8 - 5$

$1z$ is the same as $1 \times z$, or z, so $1z + 8 - 5 = z + 8 - 5$.

STEP 3 Combine the terms with no variables.

$z + 8 - 5 = z + 3$

SOLUTION

$\frac{1}{4}z + 8 + \frac{3}{4}z - 5 = z + 3$

CHECK IT OUT with the Coach™

What is the expression $5a - 6 + \frac{1}{2} - 2a + 3\frac{1}{2}$ in simplest form?

Let's check it out.

Use the commutative property of addition to rearrange the terms. Rewrite the expression. _____

Combine the terms with variables. Rewrite the expression. _____

Combine the terms with no variables. Rewrite the expression. _____

So the expression $5a - 6 + \frac{1}{2} - 2a + 3\frac{1}{2}$ in simplest form is _____.

Sample Test Questions

Simplify the expressions in Questions 1–10 by combining like terms.

1 $8m + 16m$

   A $8m$

   B $24m$

   C $24m^2$

   D $32m$

2 $n + n - 18$

   F n^2

   G -18

   H $2n - 18$

   J $n - 18$

3 $16t - 24t$

   A $-8t$

   B $8t$

   C $8t^2$

   D $40t$

4 $15d + 27d - 9d$

   F $33d^3$

   G $33d$

   H $51d^2$

   J $51d$

5 $\frac{1}{5}x + 6 + \frac{3}{5}x$

   A $\frac{4}{5}x + 6$

   B $6\frac{4}{5}x$

   C $x + 6$

   D $\frac{4}{5}x^2 + 6$

6 $a + 3a + a$

   F $5a$

   G $5 + a$

   H $3a^3$

   J $3a^2 + a$

7 $-3x + 6 - x^2 + x$

    A $-4x + 6$

    B $x^2 - 4x + 6$

    C $-x^2 - 2x + 6$

    D $-3x + 6$

8 $21y + 3 - 7y - 9$

    F $8y$

    G $24y - 16$

    H $12y - 4$

    J $14y - 6$

9 $3\frac{1}{5} + \frac{1}{5}x - \frac{4}{5}$

    Answer _____

10 $4a + 6b - 5a + 3b$

    Answer _____

Short-Response Question

11   This expression represents the area of a rectangle.

    $n^2 + 3n + 6n + 18$

Part A

Simplify the expression by combining like terms.

    Answer _____

Part B

Use what you know about combining like terms to explain why your answer is correct. Use words and/or numbers to support your explanation.

_____

_____

_____

_____

LESSON

3

Strand 2: Algebra

Solving Multi-Step Equations

7.A.4 Solve multi-step equations by combining like terms, using the distributive property, or moving variables to one side of the equation

An **equation** is a mathematical sentence using an equal (=) sign.

Examples of equations are:

$$-5x = 16x^2 \qquad z = 17 \qquad 2 + 3 = 5 \qquad y = -xy + y^2 - y^3$$

EXAMPLE 1

Solve the equation $9n + 36 = 54$.

STRATEGY

Isolate n.

STEP 1 Subtract 36 from both sides of the equation.
$$9n + 36 = 54$$
$$9n + 36 - 36 = 54 - 36$$

STEP 2 Do the math.
$$9n + 36 - 36 = 54 - 36$$
$$9n + 0 = 18$$
$$9n = 18$$

STEP 3 Multiply both sides of the equation by $\frac{1}{9}$.
$$\frac{1}{9}(9n) = \frac{1}{9}(18)$$

STEP 4 Do the math.
$$\frac{1}{9}(9n) = \frac{1}{9}(18)$$
$$n = 2$$

SOLUTION

The solution is 2.

EXAMPLE 2 Solve the equation $-2n + 7(n - 5) = 105$.

STRATEGY **Use the distributive property.**

STEP 1 Use the distributive property to multiply $7(n - 5)$.
$$7(n - 5) = 7n - 35$$

STEP 2 Rewrite the equation.
$$-2n + 7(n - 5) = 105$$
$$-2n + 7 - 35 = 105$$

STEP 3 Add the like terms.
$$-2n + 7n - 35 = 105$$
$$5n - 35 = 105$$

STEP 4 Add 35 to both sides.
$$5n - 35 = 105$$
$$5n - 35 + 35 = 105 + 35$$
$$5n + 0 = 140$$
$$5n = 140$$

STEP 5 Multiply both sides by $\frac{1}{5}$.
$$\frac{1}{5}(5n) = \frac{1}{5}(140)$$
$$n = 28$$

SOLUTION **The solution is 28.**

CHECK IT OUT with the Coach™

What is the value of x in the equation $\frac{1}{2}(2x - 8) + 2 = 35\frac{1}{2}$?

Let's check it out.

Use the distributive property. Rewrite the equation. _____

Add like terms. Rewrite the equation. _____

Add 2 to both sides. Rewrite the equation. _____

So the value of x in the equation $\frac{1}{2}(2x - 8) = 35\frac{1}{2}$ is _____.

Sample Test Questions

For Questions 1–10, solve the equation.

1 $-15 + c + 5 = 75$

A -90

B -85

C 85

D 90

2 $d - 2.7 = -2.0 + 2d$

F -4.7

G -0.7

H 0.7

J 4.7

3 $13n - 13 = 91$

A 7

B 8

C 9

D $1,014$

4 $\frac{b}{16} + 425 = 540$

F 7

G 115

H 965

J $1,840$

5 $4b + 9b - 2b = 132$

A 11

B 12

C 13

D 22

6 $\frac{t}{18} - 4 = -6$

F $-\frac{1}{9}$

G -2

H -36

J -108

7 $5n - 50 = 120$

A -34

B -14

C 14

D 34

8 $6x - 4x + 57 = 87$

F -72

G -15

H 15

J 72

9 $5x + x = \frac{6}{25}$

Answer _____

10 $5t - 2(t - 3) = 33$

Answer _____

Short-Response Question

11 A cab ride cost \$33. The equation $5m - 2 = 33$ can be used to find the number of miles m of the trip.

Part A

How many miles was the trip?

Show your work.

Answer _____ miles

Part B

Use what you know about solving equations to explain why your answer is correct. Use words and/or numbers to support your explanation.

_____

_____

_____

_____

LESSON

4

Strand 2: Algebra

Drawing Graphs of Patterns

7.A.7 Draw the graphic representation of a pattern from an equation or from a table of data
7.A.8 Create algebraic patterns using charts/tables, graphs, equations, and expressions

An equation such as $y = 3x$ has solutions that are **ordered pairs** (x, y) where the x-values are the input values and the y-values are the corresponding output values.

EXAMPLE 1

Complete the table. Then graph the ordered pairs.

x	y
1	3
2	6
3	9

STRATEGY

Find a pattern to complete the table and then graph the ordered pairs.

STEP 1 Find a pattern.

Add 1 to each x-value. Add 3 to each y-value.

STEP 2 Complete the table.

x	y
1	3
2	6
3	9
4	12
5	15

STEP 3   Graph the ordered pairs.

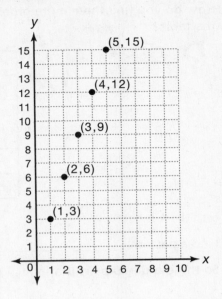

SOLUTION   **The table is shown in Step 2. The graph is shown in Step 3.**

EXAMPLE 2   List the ordered pairs from the graph. Find two more ordered pairs that match the pattern.

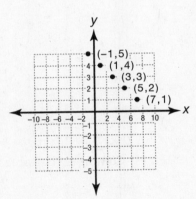

STRATEGY   **Find a pattern.**

STEP 1   List the ordered pairs.

$(-1,5), (1,4), (3,3), (5,2), (7,1)$

STEP 2   Find a pattern.

Add 2 to each x-value. Subtract 1 from each y-value.

STEP 3   Find two more ordered pairs.

$(9,0)$ and $(11,-1)$

SOLUTION   **The ordered pairs shown in the graph are $(-1,5), (1,4), (3,3), (5,2), (7,1)$. Two more ordered pairs that match the pattern could include $(9,0)$ and $(11,-1)$.**

How do you find three more ordered pairs that match the pattern in the table?

x	y
−2	−4
−1	−2
0	0
1	2
2	4

Let's check it out.

Find a pattern. _____

So three ordered pairs that match the pattern could include _____.

Sample Test Questions

1 Which ordered pair completes the table?

x	y
7	0
5	4
3	8
1	12

A (1,16)   C (1,−16)

B (−1,16)   D (−1,−16)

2 What pattern is shown in the table in Question 1?

F Add 2 to each x-value.
Subtract 4 from each y-value.

G Add 2 to each x-value.
Add 4 to each y-value.

H Subtract 2 from each x-value.
Subtract 4 from each y-value.

J Subtract 2 from each x-value.
Add 4 to each y-value.

3 Which ordered pair completes the table?

x	y
11	−3
8	−6
5	−9
2	−12

A (1,15)   C (1,−15)

B (−1,15)   D (−1,−15)

4 What pattern is shown in the table in Question 3?

F Add 3 to each x-value.
Subtract 3 from each y-value.

G Add 3 to each x-value.
Add 3 to each y-value.

H Subtract 3 from each x-value.
Subtract 3 from each y-value.

J Subtract 3 from each x-value.
Add 3 to each y-value.

5 What pattern is shown in the graph?

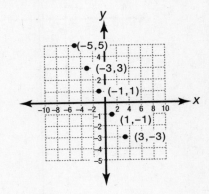

A Add 2 to each x-value.
Subtract 2 from each y-value.

B Add 2 to each x-value.
Add 2 to each y-value.

C Subtract 2 from each x-value.
Subtract 2 from each y-value.

D Subtract 2 from each x-value.
Add 3 to each y-value.

6 Which shows another ordered pair that could be on the graph in Question 5?

F (5,5)   H (−5,5)

G (5,−5)   J (−5,−5)

7 Which graph shows the ordered pair from Question 6?

A

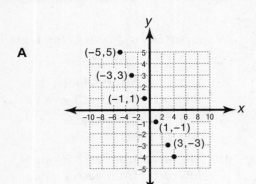

B

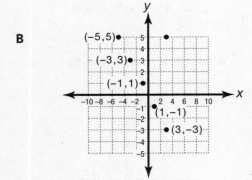

C

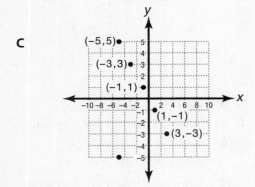

D

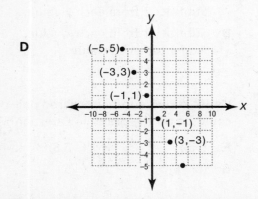

8 What pattern is shown in the graph?

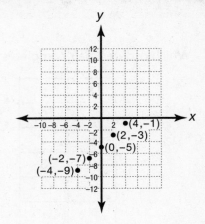

F Add 2 to each x-value.
Subtract 2 from each y-value.

G Add 2 to each x-value.
Add 2 to each y-value.

H Subtract 2 from each x-value.
Subtract 2 from each y-value.

J Subtract 2 from each x-value.
Add 2 to each y-value.

9 Which shows another ordered pair that could be on the graph in Question 8?

(6,11), (6,−11), (−6,11), (−6,−11).

Answer _____

10   Which graph shows the ordered pair from Question 9?

A

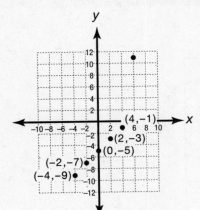

C

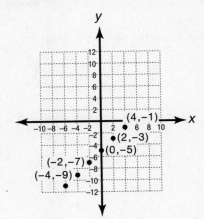

B

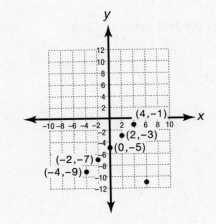

D

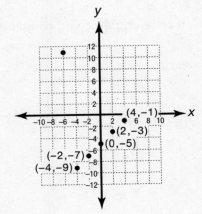

Short-Response Question

11 Look for a pattern in the table.

x	y
−2	4
−1	0
0	−4
1	−8

Part A

Which ordered pair could complete the table? Graph the five ordered pairs.

Answer _____

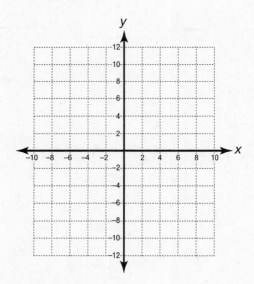

Part B

Use what you know about drawing graphs of patterns to explain why your answer is correct. Use words and/or numbers to support your explanation.

_____

_____

_____

LESSON 5

Developing Rules by Using Patterns

7.A.9 Build a pattern to develop a rule for determining the sum of the interior angles of polygons

7.A.10 Write an equation to represent a function from a table of values

Finding patterns can make solving complex problems simple.

A rule is a way to describe a pattern algebraically. To form a rule from a pattern, find the relationship between each input and output value.

EXAMPLE 1

Generate a rule to find the sum of the interior angles in a polygon.

STRATEGY

Make a table and find a pattern.

STEP 1 Make a table relating the number of sides of a polygon and the sum of the interior angles.

Number of Sides	Sum of Interior Angles (degrees)
3	180
4	360
5	540
6	720

STEP 2 Find a pattern in the table.

$180 = 1 \times 180$

$360 = 2 \times 180$

$540 = 3 \times 180$

$720 = 4 \times 180$

Look at the numbers that multiply 180. How are they related to the numbers of sides in the polygons?

STEP 3 Write the rule for the pattern.

The rule for the pattern is:

Subtract 2 from the number of sides of the polygon and multiply that number by 180.

STEP 4 Write the rule for the pattern algebraically.

Let n stand for the number of sides of the polygon.

$(n - 2) \times 180$

SOLUTION

The rule is $(n - 2) \times 180$.

EXAMPLE 2

Write the equation for the rule of the pattern in the table.

x	y
2	9
4	11
6	13
8	15

STRATEGY   **Find a pattern.**

STEP 1   Find a pattern in the table.

$2 + 7 = 9$
$4 + 7 = 11$
$6 + 7 = 13$
$8 + 7 = 15$

Each y-value is 7 more than its corresponding x-value.

STEP 2   Write the rule for the pattern algebraically.

$x + 7$

STEP 3   Write an equation showing the relationship between x and y.

$y = x + 7$

SOLUTION   **The equation is $y = x + 7$.**

EXAMPLE 3

Write the equation for the rule of the pattern in the table.

x	y
2	4
5	25
8	64
11	121

STRATEGY   **Find a pattern.**

STEP 1   Find a pattern in the table.

$2^2 = 4$
$5^2 = 25$
$8^2 = 64$
$11^2 = 121$

Each y-value is the square of its corresponding x-value.

STEP 2   Write the equation for the rule of the pattern.

$y = x^2$

SOLUTION   **The equation is $y = x^2$.**

What is the equation for the rule of the pattern in the table?

x	y
1	8
2	13
3	18
4	23

Let's check it out.

Find a pattern. _____

Write the rule for the pattern. _____

So the equation is _____.

Sample Test Questions

1 What is the rule for the pattern in the table below?

x	y
1	6
2	7
3	8
4	9

A $x + 4$ **C** $x + 5$

B $x - 4$ **D** $x - 5$

2 What is the rule for the pattern in the table below?

x	y
2	−1
4	1
6	3
8	5

F $x + 3$ **H** $x \times 3$

G $x - 3$ **J** $x \div 3$

3 What is the rule for the pattern in the table below?

x	y
0	0
2	8
4	16
6	24

A $x + 8$ **C** $x + 6$

B x^2 **D** $x \times 4$

4 What is the rule for the pattern in the table below?

x	y
1	0
2	3
3	8
4	15

F $x - 1$ **H** x^2

G $x + 1$ **J** $x^2 - 1$

5 What is the rule for the pattern in the table below?

x	y
1	3
3	7
5	11
7	15

A $x + 2$ **C** $2x + 1$

B $2x$ **D** $2x - 1$

6 What is the equation for the rule of the pattern in the table below?

x	y
1	3
4	18
7	51
10	102

F $y = x^2 + 1$ **H** $x = y^2 - 1$

G $y = x^2 + 2$ **J** $x = y^2 + 2$

7 What is the equation for the rule of the pattern in the table below?

x	y
−4	−12
−3	−9
−2	−6
−1	−3

A $y = x + 3$

B $y = x - 3$

C $y = 3x$

D $y = -3x$

8 What is the equation for the rule of the pattern in the table below?

x	y
2	−4
4	−16
6	−36
8	−64

F $y = x^2$

G $y = -x^2$

H $y = (-x)^2$

J $y = x^{-2}$

9 What is the equation for the rule of the pattern in the table below?

x	y
−8	−14
−6	−12
−4	−10
−2	−8

Answer _____

10 What is the equation for the rule of the pattern in the table below?

x	y
0	2
3	−10
6	−22
9	−34

Answer _____

Short-Response Question

11   Complete the table.

x	y
0	0
1	−4
2	−8
3	−12
4	

Part A

What is the equation for the rule of the pattern?

Answer _____

Part B

Use what you know about rules of patterns to explain why your answer is correct. Use words and/or numbers to support your explanation.

_____

_____

_____

_____

LESSON

6 | Strand 3: Geometry

Pythagorean Theorem

7.G.5 Identify the right angle, hypotenuse, and legs of a right triangle

7.G.6 Explore the relationship between the lengths of the three sides of a right triangle to develop the Pythagorean theorem

7.G.8 Use the Pythagorean theorem to determine the unknown length of a side of a right triangle

One of the most famous theorems in the history of mathematics is the **Pythagorean theorem**.

Pythagorean theorem

In any right triangle, the square of the length of the hypotenuse is equal to the sum of the squares of the lengths of the legs.

The **hypotenuse** is the side opposite the right angle. It is always the longest side of a right triangle. The two shorter sides, which form the right angle, are called legs.

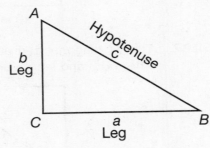

When written as a formula, the Pythagorean theorem is $a^2 + b^2 = c^2$.

You can use this formula to solve problems.

EXAMPLE 1

Identify the right angle, hypotenuse, and legs of the right triangle below.

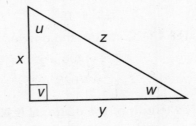

STRATEGY **Use the definition of a right triangle.**

STEP 1 A right angle measures 90°.

v is the right angle.

STEP 2 The legs are the two shortest sides of a triangle.

x and *y* are the legs.

STEP 3 The hypotenuse is the side opposite the right angle.

z is the hypotenuse.

SOLUTION **_v_ is the right angle; _x_ and _y_ are the legs; and _z_ is the hypotenuse.**

EXAMPLE 2 The length of a diagonal measures the size of a TV screen. Tanya's TV screen is 20 inches long and 15 inches wide. What is the length of the diagonal of Tanya's TV screen?

STRATEGY **Use the Pythagorean theorem.**

STEP 1 Draw a rectangle to represent the TV screen.

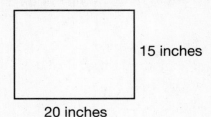

15 inches

20 inches

STEP 2 Draw a diagonal to divide the rectangle into two right triangles. The width and length become legs of the right triangle.

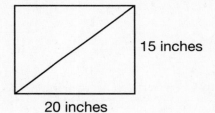

15 inches

20 inches

STEP 3 Substitute the length of the two legs in the Pythagorean theorem.

$a^2 + b^2 = c^2$

$a = 20, b = 15, c = ?$

$20^2 + 15^2 = c^2$

STEP 4 Compute the answer.

$c^2 = 400 + 225 = 625$

$c = \sqrt{625} = 25$

SOLUTION **The length of the diagonal is 25 inches.**

SPECIAL NOTE: The triangle in Example 2 is part of an important group of triangles called 3-4-5 right triangles. In this group of triangles, the lengths of the legs are multiples of the numbers 3 and 4, and the hypotenuse is a multiple of 5.

What is the length of the hypotenuse in a right triangle if the legs are 6 cm and 8 cm?

Let's check it out.

Write the Pythagorean theorem. _____

Substitute the measures of the lengths of the legs. _____

Simplify. _____

So the length of the hypotenuse is _____.

Sample Test Questions

Use the figure below to answer Questions 1 and 2.

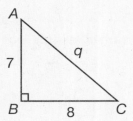

1 Which expression can you use to find the length of hypotenuse *q*?

   A $\sqrt{8^2} + \sqrt{7^2}$

   B $\sqrt{8^2 - 7^2}$

   C $\sqrt{8^2 + 7^2}$

   D $8^2 + 7^2$

2 Which names the right angle?

   F *A*

   G *B*

   H *C*

   J *q*

Use the figure below to answer Questions 3 and 4.

3 Which expression can you use to find the length of leg *q*?

   A $\sqrt{9^2 - 4^2}$

   B $\sqrt{9^2 + 4^2}$

   C $9^2 + 4^2$

   D $\dfrac{9^2 + 4^2}{2}$

4 What is the length of the hypotenuse?

   F 4

   G 9

   H 16

   J 81

5 What is the length of hypotenuse?

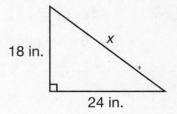

   A 6 in.

   B 12 in.

   C 30 in.

   D 36 in.

6 What is the length of side *x*?

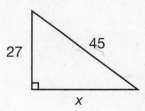

   F 6

   G 18

   H 24

   J 36

Use the figure below to answer Questions 7 and 8.

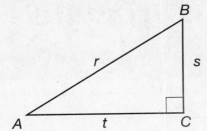

7 What is *r*?

_____

8 Which names the right angle?

_____

Short-Response Question

9 Use right triangle *ABC* below.

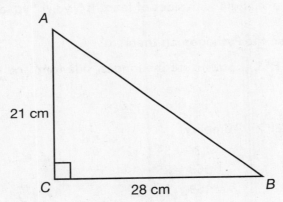

Part A

Use the Pythagorean theorem to find the length of side *AB*.

Answer _____

Part B

Use what you know about the Pythagorean theorem to explain why your answer is correct. Use words and/or numbers to support your explanation.

_____

_____

Strand 3: Geometry

Determining If a Triangle Is a Right Triangle

7.G.9 Determine whether a given triangle is a right triangle by applying the Pythagorean theorem and using a calculator

Theorem: Converse of the Pythagorean theorem

If the square of the length of the hypotenuse of a triangle is equal to the sum of the squares of the lengths of the other two legs, then the triangle is a right triangle.

If $c^2 = a^2 + b^2$, then the triangle is a right triangle.

EXAMPLE 1

Is a triangle with sides of lengths 5 yd, 12 yd, and 13 yd a right triangle?

STRATEGY   **Use the Pythagorean theorem.**

STEP 1   Substitute the longest side for c and the shorter sides for a and b.

$$c^2 = a^2 + b^2$$
$$13^2 = 5^2 + 12^2$$

STEP 2   Simplify.

$$13^2 = 5^2 + 12^2$$
$$169 = 25 + 144$$
$$169 = 169$$

SOLUTION   **A triangle with sides of lengths 5 yd, 12 yd, and 13 yd is a right triangle.**

EXAMPLE 2

Is a triangle with sides of lengths 7 cm, 8 cm, and 9 cm a right triangle?

STRATEGY   **Use the Pythagorean theorem.**

STEP 1   Substitute the longest side for c and the shorter sides for a and b.

$$c^2 = a^2 + b^2$$
$$9^2 = 7^2 + 8^2$$

STEP 2   Simplify.

$$9^2 = 7^2 + 8^2$$
$$81 = 49 + 64$$
$$81 \neq 113$$

SOLUTION   **A triangle with sides of lengths 7 cm, 8 cm, and 9 cm is not a right triangle.**

CHECK IT OUT with the Coach™

Is a triangle with sides of lengths 4.5 in., 6 in., and 7.5 in. a right triangle?

Let's check it out.

Substitute the longest side for c and the shorter sides for a and b.

_____

Simplify. _____

So a triangle with sides of lengths 4.5 in., 6 in., and 7.5 in. is _____.

Sample Test Questions

1 Which numbers can represent the side lengths of a right triangle?

A 20, 99, 101

B 10, 117, 26

C 10, 49, 50

D 2, 10, 12

2 Which numbers can represent the side lengths of the triangle shown below?

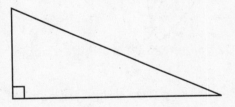

F 9, 10, 11

G 3, 4, 6

H 21, 28, 35

J 4, 5, 5

3 Which numbers can represent the side lengths of a right triangle?

A 10.5, 20.8, 23

B 39, 80, 89

C 5, 5.5, 55

D 10, 11, 14

4 Which numbers can represent the side lengths of a right triangle?

F 2, 5, 7

G 15, 30, 45

H 1, 2, 3

J 16, 30, 34

5 Which numbers can represent the side lengths of the triangle shown below?

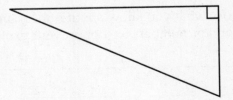

Answer

Short-Response Question

6 Jeffery flew from Cincinnati, OH, to New York, NY. Then he flew to Miami, FL, and then back to Cincinnati, OH.

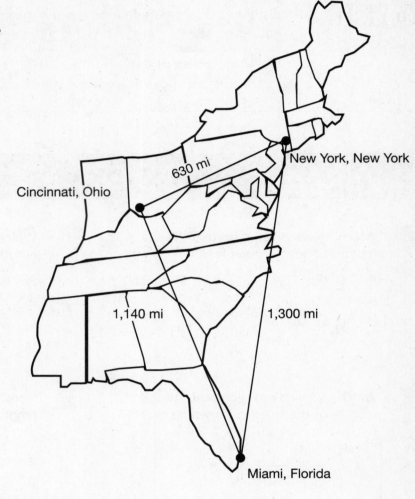

Part A

Did Jeffery's trip make a right triangle?

Answer _____

Part B

Use what you know about right triangles to explain why your answer is correct. Use words and/or numbers to support your explanation.

_____

_____

LESSON 8

Strand 4: Measurement

Calculating Distance Using a Map Scale

7.M.1 Calculate distance using a map scale

Scale drawings and scale models make it possible to show objects accurately that cannot be drawn to the correct size. Common examples of scale drawings are maps, architects' drawings, and models of homes and buildings.

In all cases, there is a numerical scale that is used to compute the actual dimensions. A scale is a ratio—the ratio between the dimensions of the drawing and the actual dimensions of the object. A proportion is when two equivalent ratios are set equal to each other.

EXAMPLE 1

On a map, Brent measured the straight-line distance between Buffalo and Auburn. The distance was 2 inches. Use the scale on the map to find the actual distance between Buffalo and Auburn.

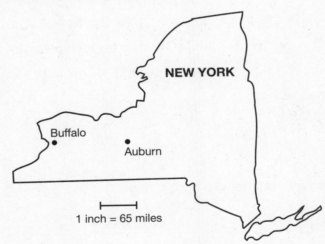

1 inch = 65 miles

STRATEGY

Make a proportion and solve it.

STEP 1 What is the scale on the map?
1 inch = 65 miles

STEP 2 Use the scale to set up a proportion.
$$\frac{1 \text{ in.}}{65 \text{ mi}} = \frac{2 \text{ in.}}{x \text{ mi}}$$

STEP 3 Solve the proportion by cross-multiplying.
$$65 \times 2 = 1 \times x$$
$$x = 130 \text{ miles}$$

SOLUTION

The actual distance from Buffalo to Auburn is 130 miles.

EXAMPLE 2

On a map, Steve measured the straight-line distance between Niagara Falls and his hometown to be 2.5 centimeters. The scale on the map shows 1 cm = 12 kilometers. What is the actual distance from Niagara Falls to Steve's hometown?

STRATEGY   **Make a proportion and solve it.**

STEP 1   Use the scale to set up a proportion.

$$\frac{1 \text{ cm}}{12 \text{ km}} = \frac{2.5 \text{ cm}}{n \text{ km}}$$

STEP 2   Solve the proportion by cross-multiplying.

$$n \times 1 = 12 \times 2.5$$
$$n = 30 \text{ km}$$

SOLUTION   **The actual distance from Niagara Falls to Steve's hometown is 30 km.**

CHECK IT OUT *with the* **Coach**™

On a map, Shelly measured the straight-line distance between Kingston, NY, and Syracuse, NY. The distance was 12.25 cm. The scale on the map shows 1 cm = 16 miles. What is the actual distance from Kingston to Syracuse?

Let's check it out.

Use the scale to set up a proportion. _____

Solve the proportion by cross-multiplying. _____

So the actual distance from Kingston to Syracuse is _____.

Sample Test Questions

1 Harold made a scale drawing of his hometown. He used the scale $\frac{1}{4}$ inch = 1 mile. The distance between the gas station and the grocery store in the drawing is 4 inches. What is the actual distance between the gas station and the grocery store?

A   1 mi

B   12 mi

C   16 mi

D   20 mi

Use the map below to answer Questions 2–6.

NEW YORK

Buffalo
Rochester

1 cm = 50 miles

Yonkers
New York City

2 The distance shown on the map between New York City and Buffalo is 5.8 cm. What is the actual distance?

F   920 mi

G   902 mi

H   290 mi

J   209 mi

3 The distance shown on the map between New York City and Rochester is 5 cm. What is the actual distance?

A   520 mi

B   502 mi

C   250 mi

D   205 mi

4 The distance shown on the map between New York City and Yonkers is 0.3 cm. What is the actual distance?

F   10 mi

G   15 mi

H   20 mi

J   25 mi

5 The distance shown on the map between Rochester and Buffalo is 1.3 cm. What is the actual distance?

A   65 mi

B   6.5 mi

C   6 mi

D   5 mi

6 The distance shown on the map between Yonkers and Rochester is 4.9 cm. What is the actual distance?

F   140 mi

G   245 mi

H   452 mi

J   542 mi

7 What is the actual distance between two cities that are $3\frac{1}{2}$ inches apart on a map with a scale of $\frac{1}{2}$ inch = 40 miles?

A   20 mi

B   40 mi

C   140 mi

D   280 mi

8 Sonya made a scale drawing of her county. She used the scale 0.5 cm = 10 km. The distance between the northernmost point and the southernmost point in the drawing is 11 cm. What is the actual distance between the two points?

F   1.1 km

G   22 km

H   110 km

J   220 km

9 The students in Greg's class made a map. The distance on the map between the school and the library was 6.5 inches. The scale was 1 inch = 50 yd. What was the actual distance from the school to the library?

Answer _____

10 Amy made a scale drawing. The distance on the map between the softball field and the gymnasium was 1.25 cm. The scale was 0.5 cm = 1 mi. What was the actual distance from the softball field to the gymnasium?

Answer _____

Short-Response Question

11 The distance on a map between two cities in 6.5 cm. The scale of the map is 1 cm = 8 km.

Part A

What is the actual distance between the two cities?

Answer _____ km

Part B

Use what you know about calculating distances using a map scale to explain why your answer is correct. Use words and/or numbers to support your explanation.

_____

_____

LESSON 9

Strand 4: Measurement

Unit Price

7.M.5 Calculate unit price using proportions
7.M.6 Compare unit prices

When you buy several items that are the same, you should know what each item costs. If you shop for different brands, you should be able to compare the prices of the different brands. A good way to compare is to find the **unit price**—the price of one item or one unit of measure.

Method 1 for Finding the Unit Price

To find the unit price for a set of items, divide the total cost by the number of items.

Method 2 for Finding the Unit Price

To find the unit price of an item of a given weight or capacity, divide the total cost by the number of units of weight or capacity.

EXAMPLE 1

Jenny spent $3.20 for 8 muffins. What is the unit price for these muffins?

STRATEGY

Use method 1.

STEP 1   What is the total cost of the muffins?
          The total cost is $3.20.

STEP 2   How many muffins did Jenny buy?
          She bought 8 muffins.

STEP 3   Use method 1 above to find the unit price.
          Divide $3.20 by 8.
          Change $3.20 to cents: $3.20 is the same as 320 cents.
          $320 \div 8 = 40$

SOLUTION

The unit price is 40 cents. This means that a single muffin costs 40 cents.

NOTE: You can also determine a unit price by writing and solving a proportion. For Example 1, this would be a proportion you could write:

$$\frac{\$3.20}{8} = \frac{x}{1}$$

Finding the unit prices of two similar items is often a good way to compare the value of the items.

EXAMPLE 2

Compare the unit prices of these two cans of soup, and determine which is the better value.

> Brand A tomato soup weighs 14 ounces and costs $2.40.
>
> Brand B tomato soup weighs 12 ounces and costs $2.15.

STRATEGY

Find the unit price of each item by using Method 2, and then compare.

STEP 1 Find the unit price of Brand A soup.

Divide the cost of Brand A soup by the weight:

$2.40 ÷ 14, or in cents, 240 ÷ 14 ≈ 17.1 cents per ounce.

STEP 2 Find the unit price of Brand B soup.

Divide the cost of Brand B soup by the weight:

$2.15 ÷ 12, or in cents, 215 ÷ 12 ≈ 17.9 cents per ounce.

STEP 3 Compare the unit prices.

17.1 cents per ounce < 17.9 cents per ounce

SOLUTION

Brand A is less expensive—it costs 17.1 cents per ounce compared with 17.9 cents for Brand B.

CHECK IT OUT *with the* **Coach**™

A pack of 12 pencils costs $2.52. What is the unit price for a pencil?

Let's check it out.

What is the total cost of the pack of pencils? _____

How many pencils are in the pack? _____

Find the unit price. _____

So the unit price for a pencil is _____.

Sample Test Questions

For Questions 1–4, find the unit price of each product. Round if necessary.

1 A dozen tomatoes cost $1.56.

  A 11 cents per tomato

  B 12 cents per tomato

  C 13 cents per tomato

  D 14 cents per tomato

2 A 17-ounce package of spaghetti costs $4.12.

  F 24 cents per ounce

  G 26 cents per ounce

  H 28 cents per ounce

  J 30 cents per ounce

3 A gallon container of apple juice sells for $4.80.

  A $1.20 per pint

  B $1.00 per pint

  C $0.60 per pint

  D $0.40 per pint

4 A package of 100 sheets of paper costs $1.50.

  F $\frac{1}{2}$ cent per sheet

  G 1 cent per sheet

  H 2 cents per sheet

  J $2\frac{1}{2}$ cents per sheet

5 A package of 20 slices of Komak American cheese costs $1.80. A package of 24 slices of Modak American cheese costs $2.64. Which cheese is the better value and by how much?

  A Komak: 2 cents per slice

  B Komak: 4 cents per slice

  C Modak: 2 cents per slice

  D Modak: 4 cents per slice

6 A box of 40 pencils from Harrow's Pencil Company costs $6.80, while a box of 50 pencils from the Carbon Pencil Company costs $9.00. Which box of pencils is the better value and by how much?

  F Harrow: 2 cents per pencil

  G Harrow: 1 cent per pencil

  H Carbon: 2 cents per pencil

  J Carbon: 1 cent per pencil

7 What is the unit price to the nearest cent of a 33-ounce bottle of juice that sells for $2.99?

  A 10 cents

  B 9 cents

  C 6 cents

  D 3 cents

8 What is the unit price to the nearest cent of a 125-pound bag of sand that sells for $82.49?

  F 65 cents

  G 66 cents

  H 82 cents

  J 83 cents

9 What is the unit price to the nearest cent of an 18-pound bag of apples that sells for $16.09?

Answer _____

10 A box of 50 notebooks from Company A costs $46.00, while a box of 75 notebooks from Company B costs $67.50. Which company has the better value, and by how much?

Answer _____

Short-Response Question

11 Brand A pasta sauce weighs 26 ounces and costs $4.99. Brand B pasta sauce weighs 32 ounces and costs $5.79.

Part A

Which brand of pasta sauce is the better buy?

Answer _____

Part B

Use what you know about unit price to explain why your answer is correct.
Use words and/or numbers to support your explanation.

_____

_____

_____

_____

LESSON

10

Strand 4: Measurement

Converting Currency

7.M.7 Convert money between different currencies with the use of an exchange rate table and a calculator

When traveling to foreign countries, it is necessary to deal with exchange currency rates. If you know the exchange rate, you can set up a proportion and cross-multiply to convert from one currency to another. Rates change on a daily basis. The table below shows some of the most common exchange rates for February 7, 2005.

USD	EUR	JPY	CAD	MXN
(U.S.—dollar)	(Europe—euro)	(Japan—yen)	(Canada—dollar)	(Mexican—peso)
1	0.78	104.55	1.26	11.18
1.28	1	133.84	1.61	14.31

EXAMPLE 1

Marcus went to Europe on vacation on February 7, 2005. He had 235 U.S. dollars. How many euros did Marcus have after he converted his U.S. dollars?

STRATEGY

Use the table to exchange U.S. dollars to euros.

STEP 1   What was the conversion factor of U.S. dollars and euros on that date?

$$1 \text{ U.S. dollar} = 0.78 \text{ euros}$$

STEP 2   Set up a proportion.

$$\frac{1}{0.78} = \frac{235}{x}$$

STEP 3   Cross-multiply to solve the proportion.

$$\frac{1}{0.78} = \frac{235}{x}$$
$$x = 0.78 \times 235$$
$$x = 183.3$$

SOLUTION

Marcus's 235 U.S. dollars converted to 183.3 euros.

EXAMPLE 2

Janet had 375 pesos on February 7, 2005. She needed to exchange this amount for U.S. dollars. How many dollars did Janet receive?

STRATEGY

Use the table to exchange pesos for U.S. dollars.

STEP 1   What was the conversion factor of U.S. dollars and pesos?

1 U.S. dollar = 11.18 pesos

STEP 2   Set up a proportion.

$$\frac{1}{11.18} = \frac{x}{375}$$

STEP 3   Cross-multiply to solve the proportion.

$$\frac{1}{11.18} = \frac{x}{375}$$

$$11.18x = 375$$

$$x = 33.54 \text{ (to the nearest cent)}$$

SOLUTION

Janet received \$33.54.

How many euros could you exchange for 82,000 yen on February 7, 2005? Use the table on p. 69.

Let's check it out.

What is the conversion factor of euros and yen? _____

Set up a proportion. _____

Solve the proportion. _____

So 82,000 yen could be exchanged for _____ euros on February 7, 2005.

Sample Test Questions

For Questions 1–10, the exchanges were made on February 7, 2005. Use the table on p. 69.

1 Amelia traveled to Europe with 512 pesos. How much did Amelia have in euros?

   A 7,326.72

   B 526.31

   C 497.69

   D 35.78

2 Eric traveled to Mexico with 125 U.S. dollars. How much did Eric have in pesos?

   F 1,397.50

   G 136.18

   H 113.82

   J 0.09

3 Beth traveled to Europe with 156 Canadian dollars. How much did Beth have in euros?

   A 96.90

   B 154.39

   C 157.61

   D 251.16

4 Doug traveled to Europe with 651 U.S. dollars. How much did Doug have in euros?

   F 5.16

   G 50.70

   H 507.78

   J 834.62

5 Andrea traveled to Canada with 255 U.S. dollars. How much did Andrea have in Canadian dollars?

   A 202.38

   B 321.30

   C 3,213

   D 32,130

6 Jun traveled to France with 364 yen. How much did Jun have in euros?

   F 2.72

   G 273.68

   H 4,818.24

   J 48,717.76

7 Kim traveled to Japan with 642 U.S. dollars. How much did Kim have in yen?

   A 671,211

   B 67,121.10

   C 61.40

   D 6.14

8 John traveled to Mexico with 362 euros. How much did John have in pesos?

   F 25.30

   G 253

   H 518.02

   J 5,180.22

9 Emily traveled to Canada with 364 euros. How much did Emily have in Canadian dollars?

Answer _____

10 Jeff traveled to Japan with 360 U.S. dollars. How much did Jeff have in yen?

Answer _____

Short-Response Question

11 Lori traveled to Europe on February 7, 2005, with 965 pesos.

Part A

How much did Lori have in euros?
Show your work.

Answer _____

Part B

Use what you know about converting currency to explain why your answer is correct. Use words and/or numbers to support your explanation.

_____

_____

_____

_____

Progress Check for Lessons 1–10

1 Which is another ordered pair that could be on the graph below?

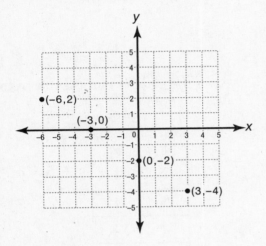

A   (6, 6)

B   (6, −6)

C   (−6, 6)

D   (−6, −6)

2 Howard traveled from Europe to the United States with 740 euros. If the exchange rate was 1 U.S. dollar for 0.78 euros, how much money did Howard have in U.S. dollars?

F $948.72

G $602.56

H $577.20

J $366.60

3 Solve for a: $7a - 15 = 15 + 5a$

A $a = 5$

B $a = 6$

C $a = 15$

D $a = 30$

4 What is the equation of the rule in the table below?

x	y
0	18
5	19
10	20
15	21

F $y = \left(\frac{x}{5}\right) + 18$

G $y = \frac{18}{(5 + x)}$

H $y = (x \times 5) + 18$

J $y = 5 \times (x + 18)$

5 A rectangular television screen measures 34 inches along its diagonal. The screen is 30 inches wide. What is the height of the screen?

A   15 in.

B   16 in.

C   17 in.

D   18 in.

6   Simplify: $n - 12 + 4n + 2 - 3n$

F $-8n$

G $10n + 14$

H $2n - 10$

J $2n + 10$

7   Solve for x: $5x - 40 = 90$

A $x = 130$

B $x = 50$

C $x = 26$

D $x = 10$

8   Which expression is a trinomial?

F $14 + x^2$

G $6 + x - x^2$

H $3 - 2x$

J x^2

9   Which numbers can represent the side lengths of a right triangle?

A   13, 14, 15

B   30, 40, 50

C   22, 33, 44

D   10, 20, 30

10   The scale on a blueprint of a house is $\frac{1}{4}$ in. = 1 ft. On the blueprint, the front of the house is $5\frac{1}{4}$ inches wide. What is the actual width of the house?

F   20 ft

G   21 ft

H   22 ft

J   23 ft

11   What is the equation for the rule of the pattern in the table?

x	y
0	$\frac{1}{2}$
1	1
2	$1\frac{1}{2}$
4	$2\frac{1}{2}$

Answer _____

12   A 30-ounce bottle of water at Cooper's mini mart cost $1.50, while a 24-ounce bottle of water at Ewing's mini mart cost $0.96. Which bottle of water is the better value and by how much?

Answer _____

OPEN-ENDED QUESTIONS

Short-Response Question

13   Randy built a ramp 15 feet long and 8 feet high.

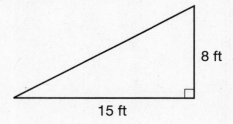

8 ft

15 ft

Part A

What is the distance of the incline of the ramp?

Show your work.

Answer _____

Part B

Use what you know about the Pythagorean theorem to explain why your answer is correct. Use words and/or numbers to support your explanation.

_____

_____

_____

_____

Extended-Response Question

14 The distance on a map between Newburgh and Massena is 8.15 cm.
The scale on the map is 1 cm = 40 miles.

Part A

What is the actual distance between Newburgh and Massena?

Show your work.

Answer _____ miles

Part B

Use what you know about scale drawings to explain why your answer to Part A is correct.
Use words and/or numbers to support your explanation.

_____

_____

_____

Part C

What scale should be used to show the cities 5 centimeters apart on the map?

Answer _____

Part D

Use what you know about scale drawings to explain why your answer to Part C is correct.
Use words and/or numbers to support your explanation.

_____

_____

_____

LESSON 11

Strand 1: Number Sense and Operations

Evaluating Expressions with Exponents

8.N.1 Develop and apply the laws of exponents for multiplication and division
8.N.2 Evaluate expressions with integral exponents

When you multiply or divide expressions involving **exponents**, these are some rules you should know.

Rules for Exponents

Rule 1: $a^s \times a^t = a^{s+t}$ for any number a and for integers s and t.
In words: When multiplying two numbers in exponent form with the same base, add the exponents. For example:
$2^3 \times 2^4 = 2^{3+4} = 2^7$

Rule 2: $(a^s)^t = a^{st}$ for any number a and for integers s and t.
In words: When raising a number with an exponent to a power, multiply the exponents. For example:
$(3^2)^5 = 3^{2 \times 3} = 3^{10}$

Rule 3: $\frac{a^s}{a^t} = a^{s-t}$ for any number a (except 0) and for integers s and t.
In words: When dividing two numbers in exponent form with the same base, subtract the exponents. For example:
$\frac{4^5}{4^2} = 4^{5-2} = 4^3$

Rule 4: $a^0 = 1$ for any number a except 0.
In words: When a number is raised to the 0 power, the result is 1. This law follows from Rule 3. For example:
$\frac{5^3}{5^3} = 5^{3-3} = 5^0$ and
$\frac{5^3}{5^3} = 1$,
so $5^0 = 1$.

Rule 5: $a^{-s} = \frac{1}{a^s}$ for any number a except 0.
In words: change the sign of an exponent by placing the exponent expression in the denominator of a fraction.
For example:
$6^{-3} = \frac{1}{6^3}$
$7^2 = \frac{1}{7^{-2}}$

These rules can help you to evaluate expressions involving exponents.

EXAMPLE 1

Find the value of $3n^2 \times 5n^3$ when $n = 2$.

STRATEGY

Use the properties of numbers, the rules for exponents, and the order of operations.

STEP 1   Simplify the expression.

$$3n^2 \times 5n^3 = 3 \times 5 \times n^2 \times n^3 \quad \text{commutative property}$$
$$= 15 \times n^{2+3} \quad\quad\quad \text{Rule 1}$$
$$= 15 \times n^5$$

STEP 2   Substitute 2 for n and use the order of operations.

$$15 \times n^5 = 15 \times 2^5 \quad\quad\quad \text{Simplify the power.}$$
$$= 15 \times 32 \quad\quad\quad \text{Multiply.}$$
$$= 480$$

SOLUTION

The value of $3n^2 \times 5n^3$ when $n = 2$ is 480.

EXAMPLE 2

Find the value of $\frac{3n^3}{27n^6}$ when $n = 4$.

STRATEGY

Use the properties of numbers, the rules for exponents, and the order of operations.

STEP 1   Simplify the expression.

$$\frac{3n^3}{27n^6} = \frac{3}{27} \times \frac{n^3}{n^6}$$
$$= \frac{3}{27} \times n^{3-6} \quad\quad\quad \text{Rule 2}$$
$$= \frac{3}{27} \times n^{-3} \quad\quad\quad \text{Rule 5}$$
$$= \frac{3}{27} \times \frac{1}{n^3}$$

STEP 2   Substitute 4 for n and simplify.

$$\frac{3}{27} \times \frac{1}{n^3} = \frac{1}{9} \times \frac{1}{4^3}$$
$$= \frac{1}{9} \times \frac{1}{64}$$
$$= \frac{1}{576}$$

SOLUTION

The value of $\frac{3n^3}{27n^6}$ when $n = 4$ is $\frac{1}{576}$.

Sometimes, you only need to substitute the value of the variable and use the **order of operations** to evaluate an expression with exponents.

EXAMPLE 3

Find the value of $-7 + (x - 5)^3 \div 9$ when $x = 2$.

STRATEGY

Substitute the value for *x* in the expression and follow the order of operations.

STEP 1   Substitute.

$$-7 + (x - 5)^3 \div 9$$
$$-7 + (2 - 5)^3 \div 9$$

STEP 2   Follow the order of operations.

$-7 + (2 - 5)^3 \div 9$	Do what is in parentheses.
$-7 + (-3)^3 \div 9$	Simplify the exponent.
$-7 + -27 \div 9$	Divide.
$-7 + -3$	Add.
-10	

SOLUTION

The value of $-7 + (x - 5)^3 \div 9$ when $x = 2$ *is* -10.

Martha's teacher gave her this expression for the area of a rectangle:

$2x^2 + 15x + 18$

Her teacher said that the value of *x* is -20.

What is the area of the rectangle?

Let's check it out.

Substitute -20 for *x* in the expression. _____

What operation should you do first? _____

What operation comes next? _____

What operation comes next? _____

Evaluate the expression.

Area of the rectangle = _____ square units

Sample Test Questions

1 Find the value of $4(3x + 2)^2$ when $x = -15$.

    A   −8,836

    B   −7,396

    C   7,396

    D   29,584

2 Find the value of $2x^3 + 9x$ when $x = -45$.

    F   −182,655

    G   −181,845

    H   181,845

    J   182,655

3 Find the value of $x^3 + 2x^2 - x$ when $x = 12$.

    A   −24

    B   2,004

    C   2,016

    D   2,028

In Questions 4–9, first simplify the expression using one or more of the rules for exponents. Then evaluate.

4 Find the value of $8n^5 \times 4n^{-3}$ when $n = 3$.

    F   −288

    G   −192

    H   192

    J   288

5 Find the value of $9n^4 \times 8n^0$ when $n = -2$.

    A   1,152

    B   144

    C   −144

    D   −1,152

6 Find the value of $\frac{36x^7}{9x^5}$ when $x = 5$.

    F $\frac{1}{100}$

    G $\frac{4}{25}$

    H   40

    J   100

7 Find the value of $\frac{12x^3}{60x^7}$ when $x = 2$.

    A $\frac{1}{80}$

    B $\frac{1}{16}$

    C $3\frac{1}{5}$

    D $204\frac{4}{5}$

8 Find and write the value of $45x^{-2} \times 4x^3 - 5x^0$ when $x = 3$.

Answer _____

9 Find the value of $\frac{5q^2}{25q^4}$ when $q = -3$. Write the answer as a fraction.

Answer _____

Short-Response Question

10 This expression represents the volume of a rectangular prism.

$$x^3 - 5x^2 + 6x$$

If $x = 8$, what is the volume of the prism?

Show your work.

Answer _____ cubic units

LESSON 12

Strand 1: Number Sense and Operations

Percents Less Than 1 and Greater Than 100

8.N.3 Read, write, and identify percents less than 1% and greater than 100%

You know that a **percent** shows the ratio of a number to 100. This lesson focuses on percents that are less than 1 and greater than 100.

When you see the expression $\frac{1}{2}$%, you read it as "one-half percent." Don't confuse $\frac{1}{2}$% with $\frac{1}{2}$, which has a value of 0.5, or 50%. One way to think about the value of a percent less than 1 is to convert the percent to an equivalent decimal.

EXAMPLE 1

What is $\frac{1}{2}$% as a decimal?

STRATEGY

Change the fraction in the percent to a decimal. Then change the decimal percent to a decimal.

STEP 1   Write the fraction in the percent as a decimal.

$\frac{1}{2} = 0.5$, so $\frac{1}{2}$% = 0.5%

STEP 2   Change the percent to a decimal.

Remember the rule: to change a percent to a decimal, move the decimal point two places to the left.

0.5% = 0.005

SOLUTION

$\frac{1}{2}$% = 0.005

Since 100% = 1, percents that are greater than 100% have a value that is greater than 1.

EXAMPLE 2

What is 400% as a decimal?

STRATEGY

Use the rule for changing a decimal to a percent.

The decimal point in 400 comes after the last zero. Move the decimal point two places to the left to change 400% to a decimal.

400% = 4.00 = 4

SOLUTION

400% = 4

What is $\frac{1}{8}$% as a decimal?

Let's check it out.

How do you write $\frac{1}{8}$ as a decimal? _____

What is $\frac{1}{8}$ as a decimal? _____

What is $\frac{1}{8}$% as a decimal percent? _____

How do you write a percent as a decimal? _____

What is the decimal percent as a decimal? _____

Sample Test Questions

1   0.4% = _____

A   0.004

B   0.04

C   0.4

D   4

2   340% = _____

F   34,000

G   34

H   3.4

J   0.34

3 $\frac{1}{5}$% = _____

A   0.2

B   0.02

C   0.002

D   0.0002

4   4500.% = _____

F   45,000

G   4,500

H   450

J   45

5 $\frac{5}{8}$% = _____

A   0.00625

B   0.0625

C   0.625

D   62.5

6 $\frac{1}{200}$ = _____

F $\frac{1}{2}$%

G $\frac{1}{20}$%

H   0.2%

J   0.02%

7 $\frac{1}{125} =$

A 800%

B 0.8%

C 0.08%

D 0.008%

8 Write 0.0004 as a percent:

Answer _____

9 Write $3\frac{1}{4}$ as a percent:

Answer _____

Short-Response Question

10 Which is a greater amount, $\frac{1}{10}$% of a cash prize or $\frac{1}{100}$ of the same cash prize?

_____

_____

_____

_____

_____

Applications of Percents

8.N.4 Apply percents to:
  Tax
  Percent increase/decrease
  Simple interest
  Sale price
  Commission
  Interest rates
  Gratuities

To find a percent of increase, you form a fraction with the amount of increase over the original amount, and change the fraction to a percent. To find a percent of decrease, you follow the procedure for finding a percent of increase, but you place the amount of decrease over the original amount.

EXAMPLE 1

In 2000, there were 240 eighth graders enrolled in Shinah's school. In 2005, there were 336 eighth graders enrolled. What was the percent of increase in enrollment?

STRATEGY

Form a fraction with the amount of increase over the original number. Then change the fraction to a percent.

STEP 1   Find the amount of increase.

enrollment in 2005 − enrollment in 2000 = 336 − 240 = 96

STEP 2   Form a fraction.

$$\frac{\text{amount of increase}}{\text{original amount}} = \frac{96}{240} = \frac{2}{5}$$

STEP 3   Change the fraction to a decimal.

$$\frac{2}{5} = 2 \times \frac{1}{5} = 2 \times 0.2 = 0.4$$

STEP 4   Change the decimal to a percent.

To change a decimal to a percent, move the decimal point two places to the right.

0.4 = 40%

SOLUTION

The percent of increase in enrollment was 40%.

If you know the percent of increase or decrease and the original amount, you can find the new amount.

EXAMPLE 2

Jared's mother said that the profit of her business this year was 300% more than last year's profit. If the profit of the business last year was $83,000, what is the profit of the business this year?

STRATEGY

Change the percent to a decimal. Then multiply and add.

STEP 1   Change the percent to a decimal.

Move the decimal point in 300% two places to the left and drop the percent sign.

300% = 3

STEP 2   Multiply last year's profit by 3.

$83,000 × 3 = $249,000

STEP 3   Add the amount of increase to last year's profit.

$83,000 + $249,000 = $332,000

SOLUTION

The profit for this year is $332,000.

Example 3 shows another applications of percent.

EXAMPLE 3

A CD that regularly costs $18 goes on sale at 25% off the regular price. What is the sale price?

STRATEGY

Change the percent to a decimal and multiply. Then subtract the product from the regular price.

STEP 1   Change the rate of discount to a decimal.

25% = 0.25

STEP 2   Multiply to find the amount of discount.

0.25 × $18 = $4.50

STEP 3   Subtract the amount of discount from the regular price.

$18 − $4.50 = $13.50

SOLUTION

The sale price is $13.50.

Simple interest is an important application of percents.

> **Formula for Simple Interest:** $I = prt$

In the formula above, I is the amount of interest (earned or paid), p is the principal (amount invested or borrowed), r is the rate expressed as a decimal, and t is the number of years the money is invested (or borrowed).

EXAMPLE 4

The Alonzo family owns a restaurant. They want to expand the restaurant, so they borrow $100,000 from a bank at 7% simple interest for 10 years. How much total interest will they pay?

STRATEGY

Use the formula for simple interest.

STEP 1   Change the rate to a decimal.

$r = 7\% = 0.07$

STEP 2   Substitute in the formula for simple interest.

$I = prt = 100,000 \times 0.07 \times 10 = 70,000$

SOLUTION

The Alonzo family will pay a total of $70,000 in interest.

CHECK IT OUT *with the* **Coach**™

Last year, Laura's parents saved $1,500 toward her college tuition. This year, they saved $2,250 toward her tuition. What was the percent increase in the amount they saved?

Let's check it out.

What is the amount of increase from last year to this year? _____

When making a fraction to show the amount of increase, over which number, 1,500 or 2,250, should you place the amount of increase? _____

What is the fraction in lowest terms? _____

What is the percent increase? _____

Sample Test Questions

1 A clothing store buys coats for $80 each and plans to sell them for $140 each. What is the percent markup on each coat?

A 25%

B 50%

C 60%

D 75%

2 What is the amount of interest that will be earned on an investment of $8,000 at 10% simple interest for 3 years?

F $2,400

G $2,500

H $2,600

J $2,800

3 Jennifer is a textbook salesperson. Last week her sales were $9,000. If her rate of commission is 14%, how much did she make in commission last week?

A $2,520

B $1,260

C $1,080

D $960

4 Mike and Cindy went to dinner at a restaurant. Their check came to $42. They want to leave a 15% tip for their waiter. How much will the total be, including tip?

F $6.30

G $43.50

H $48.30

J $57.00

5 A television has a regular price of $215. It goes on sale at a 20% discount. What is the amount of discount?

A $4.30

B $43.00

C $53.75

D $107.50

6 The Dartmouth Bank decided to increase the simple interest on savings accounts by $\frac{3}{4}$%. The current rate of interest is 3.1%. What will be the simple interest at the new rate for 2 years on an account of $20,000?

F $300

G $770

H $1,240

J $1,540

7 A computer has a selling price of $1,560. If the sales tax rate is 8.25%, what is the cost of the computer, including tax?

A $128.70

B $1,648.80

C $1,688.70

D $2,847.00

8 Last year, Lenny earned $8.00 per hour at his job. This year, he got an hourly raise of $1.20. What is the percent increase in his hourly pay?

Answer _____

9 Michel's mother wrote a mystery book for a publisher. She receives a $2\frac{1}{2}\%$ royalty on gross sales of her book. If gross sales last year were $125,000, how much money did Michel's mother receive in royalties?

Answer _____

Short-Response Question

10 Last year, there were 550 employees at a certain company. This year, there is an 18% decrease in the number of employees from last year.

How many employees are there in the company this year?

Show your work.

Answer _____

LESSON 14

Strand 1: Number Sense and Operations

Estimating Percents

8.N.5 Estimate a percent of quantity, given an application
8.N.6 Justify the reasonableness of answers using estimation

Sometimes an exact answer is not necessary, and an estimate is all you need to solve a problem. To estimate an answer, round numbers to a more convenient number, like the nearest 10. You may also want to round percents to their nearest fraction. Remember these conversions:

$$25\% = \frac{1}{4}$$

$$33\% \approx \frac{1}{3}$$

$$50\% = \frac{1}{2}$$

$$67\% \approx \frac{2}{3}$$

$$75\% = \frac{3}{4}$$

EXAMPLE 1

Joanna figures that she saves 28% when she shops at the warehouse store instead of the supermarket. Last Thursday, she spent $83 at the supermarket. If she had shopped at the warehouse store, about how much money would she have saved?

STRATEGY

Use rounding.

STEP 1 Round the percent to the nearest 10.

28% ≈ 30%

STEP 2 Round the amount of the purchase to the nearest 10.

$83 ≈ $80

STEP 3 Do the computation.

30% *of* 80 = 0.30 × 80 = 24

SOLUTION

Joanna would have saved about $24.

EXAMPLE 2

Last year, Kelvin made $204 per week at his job. This year, he got a raise of $31 per week. What is a good estimate of the percent of increase in his weekly pay?

STRATEGY

Find numbers close to 204 and 31 that form a fraction that is easy to convert to a percent.

STEP 1   Find numbers that are close to 204 and 31.

$204 \approx 200$ and $31 \approx 30$

STEP 2   Write a fraction and convert it to a percent.

$$\text{Rate of increase} = \frac{\text{increase in pay}}{\text{original pay}} = \frac{30}{200}$$

$$= \frac{15}{100}$$

$$= 15\%$$

SOLUTION

A good estimate of the rate of increase in his weekly pay is 15%.

You can verify the results in Example 2 by using the actual numbers and a calculator:

$$\frac{31}{204} \approx 0.152$$

$$0.152 = 15.2\%$$

Since 15% is close to 15.2%, the estimate of 15% is accurate.

EXAMPLE 3

The Johnson family went out to dinner at a restaurant. The total bill came to $78.59. They want to leave a 15% tip. About how much money should they leave?

STRATEGY

Round $78.59 to a convenient whole number. Then use the fact that 15% = 10% + 5%.

STEP 1   Round $78.59.

$78.59 is about $80.

STEP 2   Use the fact that 15% = 10% + 5%.

10% of $80 = 0.1 × 80 = $8

5% is half of 10%, so 5% of the bill is half of $8, or $4.

(10% of $80) + (5% of $80) = $8 + $4 = $12

SOLUTION

The Johnson family should leave a tip of about $12.

You can use estimation to check calculations done with pencil and paper or with a calculator.

EXAMPLE 4

There are 38,400 registered voters in a town. The local newspaper reported that only 25% of registered voters voted in the last election. Arthur used his calculator to find the number of people who voted and got 1,536. Is Arthur's answer reasonable?

STRATEGY

Estimate the answer and compare the result with Arthur's.

Round 38,400 to 40,000.

Think of 25% as $\frac{1}{4}$.

So 25% of 38,400 $\approx \frac{1}{4} \times 40,000 = 10,000$

SOLUTION

Arthur's answer is not reasonable because 1,536 is not close to 10,000. (It appears that Arthur divided 38,400 by 25 when he should have multiplied 38,400 by 0.25.)

CHECK IT OUT *with the* **Coach**

The eighth-grade enrollment at Clara's middle school increased by 32% from 2000 to 2005. There were 273 eighth graders enrolled in 2000. About how many more eighth graders were enrolled in 2005 than in 2000?

Let's check it out.

What is 32% rounded to the closest fraction? _____

What is 273 rounded to the nearest 10? _____

What must you do with the rounded amounts to find the increase in

enrollment? _____

About how many more eighth graders were enrolled in 2005? _____

Sample Test Questions

1 Last year, the school computer club had 148 members. This year the computer club has 121 members. Which of the following is the best estimate of the percent decrease in membership?

A 15%

B 20%

C 25%

D 30%

2 There are 494 students enrolled in an elementary school. On Monday, about 19% of the students were on a field trip. Which is the best estimate of the number of students who were on field trips on Monday?

F 40

G 60

H 80

J 100

3 A computer that had a regular price of $794 was on sale at a discount of 25%. Ralph used his calculator to find the amount of discount and got $19.35. Which of the following could he use to check his result?

A $800 \div \frac{1}{4}$

B $800 \times \frac{1}{4}$

C 800×2.5

D $800 \div 25$

4 In the year 1990, the population of the town where Cindy lives was 1,507. By the year 2000, there were 148 more people living in the town. Which of the following is the best estimate of the percent of increase in the population?

F 5%

G 10%

H 15%

J 20%

5 Mr. Johnson invested $12,000 in a mutual fund. The rate of return in the past year for the fund was 9.4%. Assuming that the rate of return will be the same this year, Mr. Johnson used a calculator to find that the investment would earn $1,128. What is a good estimate Mr. Johnson can use to check his calculator result?

A $1,294

B $1,200

C $120

D $94

6 On a certain restaurant menu, it states that for parties of 6 or more, a tip of 18% is added to the check. Lucy and 5 of her friends ordered food and beverages that came to $187.20. Which is the best estimate of the amount the restaurant added to the check?

F $20

G $40

H $60

J $80

7 A new cellular phone has a retail price of $249.99. Melvin is signing up for a calling plan that will give him a 60% discount on the phone. Which of the following is the best estimate of the amount he will pay for the phone?

A $60

B $100

C $140

D $180

8 The restaurant bill for Keisha's birthday party came to $419.50. She wants to leave a tip of 18% for the waiters. What is a good estimate she can use to check a calculator result?

F $32

G $80

H $320

J $800

9 Carlos estimates that he spends 75% of every study period concentrating on his work. If his last study period lasted 46 minutes, about how long did he concentrate on his work?

A 10 minutes

B 25 minutes

C 35 minutes

D 40 minutes

Short-Response Question

10 Your friend uses a calculator to find 24% of $1,195 and gets $2,868.80. Is your friend's answer reasonable? Explain your answer.

_____

_____

_____

_____

_____

_____

_____

Progress Check for Lessons 11–14

1 What is the value of x^{-5} when $x = 2$?

   A $-\frac{1}{10}$

   B $-\frac{1}{32}$

   C $\frac{1}{32}$

   D $\frac{1}{10}$

2 What is the selling price of an $899 computer system that is on sale at a 25% discount?

   F $224.75

   G $649.50

   H $674.25

   J $824.50

3 How much will an investment of $6,000 earn if it is invested for 4 years in an account that pays 5% simple interest?

   A $75

   B $120

   C $300

   D $1,200

4 The number of people who work for the MBI Company now is 310% more than the number of people who worked there ten years ago. If 240 people worked for the MBI Company ten years ago, how many people work for the company now?

   F   564   **H**   744

   G   644   **J**   984

5 Which of the following is equivalent to $\frac{3}{8}$%?

   A   0.375

   B   0.0375

   C   0.00375

   D   0.000375

6 Find the value of $x^2 - 10x + 25$ when $x = -15$.

   F -350 **H**   250

   G -50 **J**   400

7 In a survey of 505 people, about 57% said that they would reelect the mayor. Which is the best estimate of the number of people in the survey who said they would reelect the mayor?

   A   250   **C**   350

   B   300   **D**   400

8 Last week, Lorinda earned $604. She predicts that this week she will earn 38% more money than she did last week. Using a calculator, she found that her total earnings next week would be $833.52. Which of the following is a good way for her to find an estimate to check that that her calculator result is reasonable?

   F $600 \times 0.4 + 600$

   G $600 \times 4 - 400$

   H $600 \div 4 + 600$

   J $600 \div 40 + 600$

Short-Response Question

9   What is the value of $\frac{16x^7}{40x^5}$ when $x = 5$?

Show your work.

Answer _____

Extended-Response Question

10   A discount department store is offering a $1,995 home theater system at a 50% discount.

Part A

What is a good estimate of the selling price of the system?

Estimate _____

Part B

What is the actual selling price?

Answer _____

Part C

Another discount store was offering the same home theater system at a 30% discount. When the second store discovered the discount the first store was giving, the second store discounted its already discounted price by another 20%. What was the selling price of the system at the second store after the two successive discounts of 30% and 20%?

Show your work.

Answer _____

Part D

Which store had the lower price for home theater system?

Answer _____

LESSON 15

Strand 2: Algebra

Matching Verbal Expressions to Algebraic Expressions

8.A.2 Write verbal expressions that match given mathematical expressions

An algebraic expression is a model of a verbal expression with numbers and variables.

EXAMPLE

If n represents a number of baseball cards, which verbal expression does this algebraic expression model?

$2n - 3$

A   twice the number of baseball cards

B   three more than twice the number of baseball cards

C   two more than three times the number of baseball cards

D   three fewer than twice the number of baseball cards

STRATEGY   **Compare each choice with the given expression.**

STEP 1   Consider choice A.

"Twice the number of baseball cards" means that the number of cards is multiplied by 2. But the expression also shows another operation, so this choice is not correct.

STEP 2   Consider choice B.

"Three more than twice the number of baseball cards" means that the number of cards is multiplied by 2 ("twice") and then 3 is added ("three more"). The expression shows that 3 is subtracted, so this choice is not the correct one.

STEP 3   Consider choice C.

"Two more than three times the number of baseball cards" means that the number of cards is multiplied by 3 ("three times") and then 2 ("two more") is added. The expression shows the numbers reversed.

STEP 4   Consider choice D.

"Three fewer than twice the number of baseball cards" means that 3 is subtracted ("three fewer") from 2 times ("twice") the number of baseball cards. This matches the given expression.

SOLUTION   **The verbal expression that matches $2n - 3$ is "three fewer than twice the number of baseball cards", choice D.**

CHECK IT OUT *with the* **Coach**™

In the following algebraic expression, *x* represents a number of amusement park ride tickets.

$15x + 10$

What is a verbal expression that matches the algebraic expression?

Let's check it out.

What does $15x$ mean in words? _____

What does $+ 10$ mean in words? _____

What is a verbal expression that matches $15x + 10$? _____

Sample Test Questions

For Questions 1–7, choose the verbal expression that matches the given algebraic expression.

1 $6n \div 4$

   A   the product of four times a number and six

   B   the product of six times a number and four

   C   the quotient of six times a number and four

   D   the quotient of four and six times a number

2 $\frac{2}{3}x - 9$

   F   nine less than two-thirds of a number

   G   nine more than two-thirds of a number

   H   the product of two thirds of a number and negative nine

   J   two thirds times the difference of a number and nine

3 $-7(a + 3)$

   A   the product of negative seven and the difference of a number and three

   B   the product of negative seven and the sum of a number and three

   C   three more than the product of a number and negative seven

   D   seven less than the sum of a number and three

4 $\frac{n + 15}{5}$

   F   five less than the product of a number and fifteen

   G   the quotient of fifteen and five, increased by a number

   H   the product of a number and fifteen, divided by five

   J   the sum of a number and fifteen, divided by five

5 The variable *n* represents the number of attendees at last week's soccer game.

$2n + 30$

A two more than thirty times the number of attendees at last week's game

B thirty fewer than twice the number of attendees at last week's game

C the difference of twice the number of attendees at last week's game and thirty

D thirty more than twice the number of attendees at last week's game

6 The variable *s* stands for the number of units in one side of a square.

$4s - 4$

F the perimeter of the square increased by 4 units

G the perimeter of the square decreased by 4 units

H four times the perimeter of the square increased by 4 units

J the product of 4 and the perimeter of the square

7 The variable *d* represents the number of dollars in a bank account.

$\frac{1}{2}d - 10$

A ten dollars less than half the number of dollars in the account

B one half the difference of the dollars in the account and ten dollars

C one half the number of dollars in the account increased by ten dollars

D the product of half the dollars in the account and negative ten dollars

8 Write an algebraic expression that stands for this phrase:

six years younger than twice Daniel's age

Answer _____

9 Represent this phrase algebraically:

two fewer than one-third of the school's vans are out of commission

Answer _____

Short-Response Question

10 The variable *m* represents the number of members in the science club. Write a verbal description that matches this algebraic expression.

$8m - 12$

_____

_____

LESSON 16

Strand 2: Algebra

Translating Words into Inequalities

8.A.1 Translate verbal expressions into algebraic inequalities

Many problem situations can be translated into mathematical sentences. A mathematical sentence may be an equation or an **inequality**. This lesson will focus on algebraic inequalities. Look for key words in a problem that translate into inequality symbols such as *is greater than* ($>$), *is less than* ($<$), *is at least* ($\geq$), and *is at most* ($\leq$).

EXAMPLE 1

Tim is in charge of buying cans of juice for a class picnic. He has 14 cans of juice left over from the last picnic. He can buy cans of juice in six-packs. He wants to have at least 80 cans of juice for the picnic. Write an inequality that can be used to find how many six-packs he will have to buy.

STRATEGY   **Look for key words in the problem.**

STEP 1   Choose a variable to represent the number of six-packs.

Let n = the number of six-packs.

STEP 2   Translate the problem into a sentence.

If one six-pack contains 6 cans, then n six-packs contain $6n$ cans.

He wants a total of at least 80 cans, so use the symbol $\geq$.

number of cans he needs to buy +
number of cans he already has $\geq$ 80 cans

$$6n + 14 \geq 80$$

SOLUTION   **An inequality for finding the number of six-packs he needs to buy is $6n + 14 \geq 80$.**

EXAMPLE 2

A group of friends wants to hire a limousine for the senior dance. They do not want to spend any more than $300. The limousine service charges a basic fee of $45 plus $50 per hour. Write an inequality to find the number of hours they can hire the limousine.

STRATEGY   **Look for key words in the problem.**

STEP 1   Choose a variable to represent the number of hours they can hire the limousine.

Let h = the number of hours.

STEP 2   Translate the problem into a sentence.

If one hour costs $50, then h hours costs $50h$.

They want to spend no more than $300, so use the symbol $\leq$.

amount of money at $50 per hour +
basic fee of the limousine $\leq$ $300

$$50h + 45 \leq 300$$

SOLUTION   **An inequality for finding the number of hours they can hire the limousine is $50h + 45 \leq 300$.**

CHECK IT OUT *with the* **Coach**™

Natalie has $48 saved so far for spending money for her vacation. She wants to have more than $200 in spending money. She has 6 more weeks until her vacation. What inequality can you write to find the average amount she will have to save each week to reach her goal?

Let's check it out.

Choose a variable to represent the amount she needs to save each week.

_____

Write an expression for how much she can save in 6 weeks, not counting the amount she has already saved. _____

Write an expression for how much she can save, including the $48 she has already saved. _____

Since she wants more than a total of $200, which inequality symbol will you use? _____

Write an inequality for finding the average amount she will have to save each week. _____

Sample Test Questions

1 As part of his fitness program, Sam wants to run a total of more than 20 miles this week. He has already run 14 miles. There are 2 days remaining in the week. If he runs the same number of miles on each of those 2 days, which inequality can be used to find n, the number of miles he must run on each of those 2 days?

A $2n + 20 > 14$

B $2n + 14 < 20$

C $2n - 14 > 20$

D $2n + 14 > 20$

2 Vicky works in an appliance store. She earns $50 per day plus $4 for each appliance she sells. She is hoping to make at least $150 today. Which inequality can be used to find n, the number of appliances she will have to sell?

F $4n + 50 \geq 150$

G $4n - 50 \geq 150$

H $50 - 4n \geq 150$

J $50 + (n + 4) \geq 150$

3 The quotient of a number and 14 is no greater than 112. Which inequality can be used to find n, the number?

A $n \div 14 < 112$

B $n \div 14 \geq 112$

C $n \div 14 > 112$

D $n \div 14 \leq 112$

4 Sarah wants to have at least $75 to go shopping for an anniversary gift for her parents. She has already saved $30. She plans to save $15 per week. Which inequality can you use to find w, the number of weeks she will need to save to achieve her goal?

F $w + 30 \geq 75$

G $15w + 30 \geq 75$

H $30w + 15 \geq 75$

J $15w - 30 \geq 75$

5 A concert hall has a legal capacity of 1,200. So far, 875 tickets have been sold for a concert next week. Tickets will be on sale for 5 more days. Which inequality can you use to find t, the average number of tickets the hall can sell each day and still keep the total number of tickets within the legal limit?

A $5t \times 875 \leq 1,200$

B $5t - 875 \leq 1,200$

C $5t + 875 \leq 1,200$

D $5(t + 875) \leq 1,200$

6 Paul earns $25 per hour at his job. Each day, he spends $6 for roundtrip carfare and $9 for lunch. Today, he wants to take home at least $200 after paying for his lunch and carfare. Which inequality can you use to find h, the number of hours he will have to work to achieve his goal?

F $25h + 15 \geq 200$

G $25(h + 15) \geq 200$

H $25h - 15 \geq 200$

J $25(h - 15) \geq 200$

7 Wendy said, "I'm thinking of a set of whole numbers. If you divide any of these numbers by 8 and then increase the result by 5, the result is less than 77." Which inequality can you use to find this set of numbers?

A $n \div (8 + 5) < 77$

B $n \div 8 + 5 < 77$

C $n \div 5 + 8 < 77$

D $n \div 8 - 5 < 77$

8 Last year, an eighth-grade class collected 170 pounds of metal for recycling. So far, this year's eighth-grade class has collected 106 pounds of metal for recycling. There are 4 weeks remaining in the recycling drive. Which inequality can you use to find n, the average number of pounds of metal per week that this year's class must collect in order to exceed last year's total?

Answer _____

9 Ibrahim is reading a long book. He has read 125 pages and wants to finish more than 350 pages in the next 4 hours. Write an inequality that shows the average number of pages he has to read per hour to reach his goal.

Answer _____

Short-Response Question

10 A high school class is planning its annual hayride. There is a flat fee of $50 plus $30 per hour to hire the hay wagon. The class has a budget of $280 for the hayride.

Part A

Write an inequality to find h, the number of hours they can hire the hay wagon and stay within the budget.

_____

Part B

Explain how you determined the equation you wrote in Part A.

_____

_____

_____

LESSON 17

Strand 2: Algebra

Matching Graphs to Situations

8.A.3   Describe a situation involving relationships that matches a given graph

8.A.4   Create a graph given a description or an expression for a situation involving a linear or nonlinear relationship

8.A.16 Find a set of ordered pairs to satisfy a given linear numerical pattern (expressed algebraically); then plot the ordered pairs and draw the line

A graph can give information about real–life events.

EXAMPLE 1

Julia drove to visit her cousin who lives 160 miles away. She began her drive at 9:00 A.M. This graph shows Julia's progress during the trip.

$$\frac{25x^5}{-3x^2} + \frac{18x^3}{-3x^2} + \frac{12x^3}{-3x^2}$$

$$-9x^3 + -6x + 4$$

$$-9x^3 - 6x + 4$$

a. When was Julia on the highway?

b. When did she have lunch?

c. When did she travel on local roads?

STRATEGY

Study the changes in the line graph.

a. When was Julia on the highway?

Julia would probably be driving fast on the highway. The portion of the graph from 10:00 A.M. to 12:00 noon is the steepest. She drove 120 miles in this 2-hour period, so she averaged 60 miles per hour. So, it is likely that she was on the highway from 10:00 A.M. to 12:00 noon.

b. When did she have lunch?

There is a horizontal line segment from 12:00 noon to 1:00 P.M. This indicates that Julia did not cover any distance during this hour. So it would be reasonable to assume that she stopped the car and had lunch.

c. When did she travel on local roads?

Julia would probably be driving slowly on local roads. She drove 20 miles from 9:00 A.M. to 10:00 A.M., so she averaged 20 miles per hour. This is a reasonable speed for local roads. She also drove just 20 miles from 1:00 P.M. to 2:00 P.M., so it is likely that she was on local roads during this hour as well.

SOLUTION

Julia was on the highway from 10:00 A.M. to 12 noon; she stopped for lunch from 12:00 noon to 1:00 P.M.; and she was on local roads from 9:00 A.M. to 10:00 A.M. and from 1:00 P.M. to 2:00 P.M.

Some situations can be expressed as **linear equations**. The graph of a linear equation is a straight line. By substituting a value for one variable in a linear equation, you can find the value of the other variable. Each pair of these values is called an **ordered pair** and can be graphed on a coordinate plane. Ordered pairs are written in the form (x, y).

EXAMPLE 2

Jamal bought a plant that was 3 centimeters tall. He recorded its height each week and used his data to write this equation for describing the plant's growth:

$y = 2x + 3$

In Jamal's equation, x represents the number of weeks, and y represents the height of the plant in centimeters.

Graph Jamal's equation.

STRATEGY   **Make a table of ordered pairs. Then graph the ordered pairs and connect the points.**

STEP 1   Make a table.

Choose values for x and substitute them in the equation to find corresponding values for y.

x	y = 2x + 3	y	(x,y)
0	y = 2(0) + 3 = 0 + 3 = 3	3	(0,3)
1	y = 2(1) + 3 = 2 + 3 = 5	5	(1,5)
2	y = 2(2) + 3 = 4 + 3 = 7	7	(2,7)
3	y = 2(3) + 3 = 6 + 3 = 9	9	(3,9)

STEP 2   Graph the ordered pairs and draw a line through the points starting with the point at (0,3).

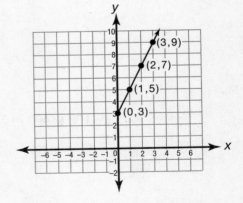

The graph of the equation $y = 2x + 3$ extends indefinitely in both directions. In the given situation about the number of weeks and the heights of the plant, however, it would not make sense to show solutions where x-values and/or y-values are negative. Therefore, only the parts of the line where $x \geq 0$ and $y > 0$ are graphed.

SOLUTION   **Step 2 shows the graph of Jamal's equation.**

When the situation describing a linear equation does not limit the x- or y-values, you should graph the complete line.

EXAMPLE 3

Graph the equation $y = -2x + 4$.

STRATEGY

Graph several ordered pairs and connect them with a straight line.

STEP 1   Make a table of x-values and y-values to find three or four ordered pairs.

x	$y = -2x + 4$	y	(x,y)
0	$y = -2(0) + 4 = 0 + 4 = 4$	4	(0,4)
1	$y = -2(1) + 4 = -2 + 4 = 2$	2	(1,2)
2	$y = -2(2) + -4 = 4 + 4 = 0$	0	(2,0)
3	$y = -2(3) + 4 = -6 + 4 = -2$	-2	(3,-2)

STEP 2   Graph the ordered pairs and draw a straight line through the points.

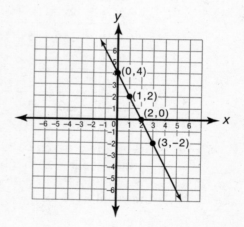

SOLUTION

The graph in Step 2 is the graph of $y = -2x + 4$.

CHECK IT OUT *with the* **Coach**™

How do you graph the linear equation *y* = *x* − 3?

Let's check it out.

Start by completing the table.

x	y = x − 3	y	(x,y)
0	y = (0) − 3 = −3		
1	y = (1) − 3 = −2		
2	y = (2) − 3 = −1		
3	y = (3) − 3 = 0		

Graph the ordered pairs as points on this grid.

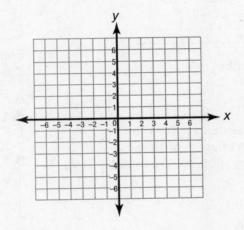

What must you do to the points to complete the graph of the equation?

_____

Complete the graph above.

Sample Test Questions

The graph below shows this situation: Kyle left his house at 1:00 P.M. and walked to Michael's house. Michael's house is 900 yards from Kyle's house. Use the graph to answer Questions 1–3.

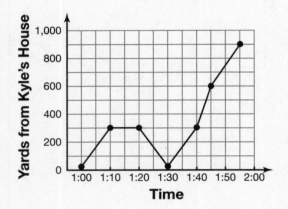

1 Kyle walked at the same pace for most of his trip. For a short period of time, he picked up his pace by jogging. When did he jog?

A from 1:00 to 1:10

B from 1:10 to 1:20

C from 1:30 to 1:40

D from 1:40 to 1:45

2 What could have happened from 1:10 to 1:20?

F He walked faster than he walked from 1:00 to 1:10.

G He stopped at a store to buy a present for Michael's mother.

H He made a right turn from the path he walked on from 1:00 to 1:10.

J He walked back home to make sure he had locked the door.

3 On his way to Michael's house, Kyle realized that he forgot to lock his front door, so he had to return home. When did he get home?

A 1:00

B 1:20

C 1:30

D 2:00

4 A construction company took a long time to finish the foundation and the first 4 floors of an office building. The company's contract with the building's owner states that from now on, the construction company must complete 2 floors per week. An equation that describes the situation is $y = 2x + 4$ where x represents the number of weeks and y represents the total number of completed floors of the office building. Which graph shows this situation?

F

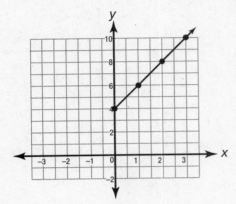

H

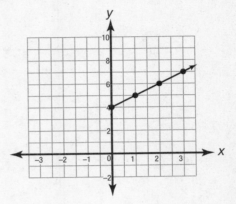

G

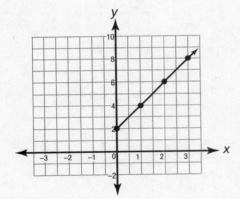

J

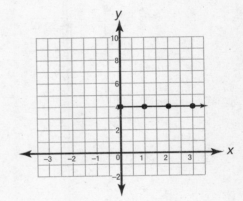

5 Which is the graph of the linear equation $y = x - 2$?

A

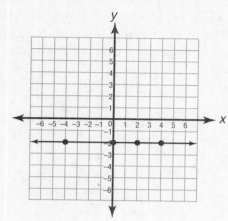

C

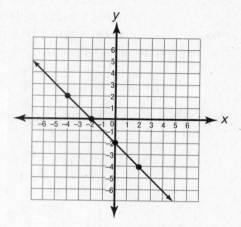

B

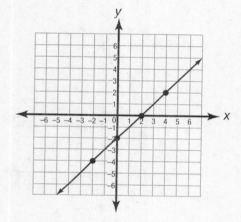

D

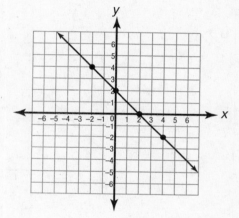

6   Which is the graph of the linear equation $y = 2x - 5$?

F

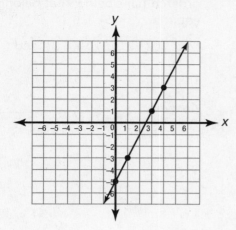

H

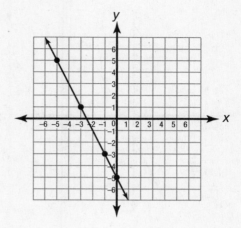

G

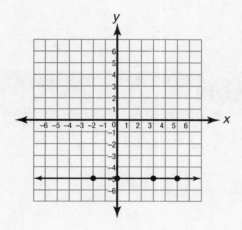

J

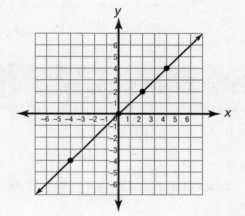

7   Which equation has this graph?

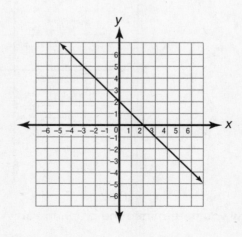

A $y = x + 2$

B $y = 2x + 2$

C $y = -x + 2$

D $y = -x - 2$

8 What equation has this graph?

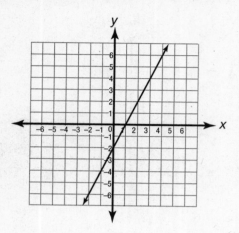

Answer _____

9 Write the missing number for the four ordered pairs below that belong to this equation: $y = 5x - 6$

$(2, \underline{\hspace{1cm}}), (-2, \underline{\hspace{1cm}}), (0, \underline{\hspace{1cm}})$, and $(-10, \underline{\hspace{1cm}})$

Answer _____

Short-Response Question

10

Part A

Graph the equation $y = -2x + 3$ on the coordinate grid below.

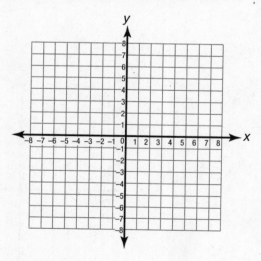

Part B

Explain how you determined the graph in Part A.

_____

Strand 2: Algebra

Adding and Subtracting Polynomials

8.A.7 Add and subtract polynomials (integer coefficients)

In mathematics, a **term** is a number, a variable, or the product of a number and one or more variables. A term by itself is called a **monomial**. Here are some examples of monomials.

$$3 \qquad x \qquad 5x \qquad 12n^2 \qquad -4ab$$

A **polynomial** is a sum or difference of monomials. Here are some examples.

$$b^2 - 2b \qquad\qquad x^2 - 8x + 15 \qquad\qquad d^3 + 2d^2 + 5d - 7$$

A **binomial** is a polynomial with two terms. For example:

$$x + 25 \qquad\qquad 16n^2 - 81 \qquad\qquad x^3 + y^3$$

A **trinomial** is a polynomial with three terms. For example:

$$k^2 + 2k + 1 \qquad\qquad 6n^2 + n - 12$$

You can add and subtract polynomials by combining **like terms**. Like terms have the same variables raised to the same powers. Here are some examples.

$$7x \text{ and } -2x \qquad\qquad 15y^2 \text{ and } 4y^2 \qquad\qquad -8ab \text{ and } ab$$

To combine like terms, add their numerical coefficients. In the examples above, the numerical coefficients of $7x$ and $-2x$ are 7 and -2; the numerical coefficients of $15y^2$ and $4y^2$ are 15 and 4; the numerical coefficients of $-8ab$ and ab are -8 and 1 (remember, $ab = 1ab$).

EXAMPLE 1

Add the binomials: $(2x + 3y) + (5x + 6y)$.

STRATEGY

Combine the like terms.

STEP 1   Arrange the polynomials vertically with like terms in the same column.

$$2x + 3y$$
$$5x + 6y$$

STEP 2   Add the terms in the columns.

Combine the numerical coefficients.

$2x + 3y$

$5x + 6y$

$7x + 9y$

SOLUTION   **$(2x + 3y) + (5x + 6y) = 7x + 9y$**

EXAMPLE 2   Subtract: $(3x^2 + 4x + 7) - (x^2 - 4)$

STRATEGY   **Combine like terms.**

STEP 1   Use the definition of subtraction to rewrite the second polynomial.

When you subtract, you add the opposite of the number that is being subtracted. So if you are subtracting $(x^2 - 4)$, you should add the opposite of the polynomial.

$(3x^2 + 4x + 7) - (x^2 - 4) = (3x^2 + 4x + 7) + -(x^2 - 4)$

STEP 2   Simplify $-(x^2 - 4)$.

A negative sign in front of a polynomial in parentheses changes the sign of each term of the polynomial.

$-(x^2 - 4) = -x^2 + 4 = -1x^2 + 4$

STEP 3   Arrange the polynomials vertically with like terms in the same column and add.

$$\begin{array}{r} 3x^2 + 4x + 7 \\ -1x^2 \qquad + 4 \\ \hline 2x^2 + 4x + 11 \end{array}$$

SOLUTION   **$(3x^2 + 4x + 7) - (x^2 - 4) = 2x^2 + 4x + 11$**

CHECK IT OUT with the Coach™

The area of one rectangular lot is represented by the polynomial $2x^2 + 9x + 10$, and the area the lot next to it is represented by the polynomial $x^2 - 6x + 9$. What is an expression for the area of the two lots combined?

Let's check it out.

What operation will you use on the polynomials? _____

How can you arrange the polynomials to make it easier to combine their

terms? _____

What is an expression for the combined areas? _____

Sample Test Questions

1 $(7r + 3s) + (4r + 8s) =$ _____

  A $11rs$

  B $11r + 11s$

  C $10rs + 12rs$

  D $10r + 12s$

2 $(3xy - 10) - (xy + 5) =$ _____

  F $2xy - 15$

  G $2xy + 15$

  H $2xy + 5$

  J $3xy + 15$

3 $(a^2 + 2ab + b^2) +$
$(4a^2 - 4ab + b^2) =$ _____

  A $4a^2 + 6ab + 2b^2$

  B $4a^2 - 2ab + b^2$

  C $5a^2 - 2ab + 2b^2$

  D $5a^2 + 2ab + 2b^2$

4 $(9x^3 - 6x^2 - 3x + 1) +$
$(5x^3 + 7x^2 + 3x + 1) =$ _____

  F $14x^3 + 13x^2 + 2$

  G $14x^3 + x^2 + 2$

  H $14x^3 - x^2 + 6x + 2$

  J $14x^3 - 13x^2 - 6x + 2$

5 $(10c - 17) - (4c + 17) =$ _____

  A $14c + 34$

  B $6c$

  C $6c - 34$

  D $6c + 34$

6 $(-5y^2 + y - 4) - (4y^2 + y + 3) =$ _____

  F $-9y^2 - 7$

  G $-9y^2 + 2y - 1$

  H $-9y^2 + 2y + 7$

  J $y^2 + 2y - 7$

7 $(6a + 2b - 5c) - (3a + 2c) =$ _____

  A $9a + 2b + 3c$

  B $3a - 2b - 3c$

  C $3a + 2b + 7c$

  D $3a + 2b - 7c$

8 Write the answer.

$(8x^2 + 5) - (6x^2 + 4x + 10) =$ _____

Answer _____

9 Write the answer.

$(17t^4 + 4t^2) - (9t^3 - 4t^2) =$ _____

Answer _____

Short-Response Question

10 The area of the rectangular mirror on Muriel's wall is $(x^2 + 5x + 6)$ square units. She wants to replace the mirror with a new, larger mirror whose area is $(6x^2 + 7x + 2)$ square units.

Find an expression for how much larger the new mirror is than the old mirror.

Show your work.

Answer _____ square units

LESSON 19

Strand 2: Algebra

Multiplying and Dividing by Monomials

8.A.6 Multiply and divide monomials
8.A.9 Divide a polynomial by a monomial (integer coefficients)

When you multiply two monomials, you multiply the numerical coefficients and then multiply the variables. If the variables are the same, you use the rule for multiplying two numbers in exponent form with the same base; that is, you add the exponents. (See Lesson 11 if you need to review this rule.)

EXAMPLE 1

Multiply: $(7x^2)(-3x^3)$

STRATEGY

Multiply the numerical coefficients and multiply the variables.

STEP 1   Multiply the numerical coefficients.

$$7 \cdot -3 = -21$$

STEP 2   Multiply the variables.

$$x^2 \cdot x^3 = x^{2+3} = x^5$$

STEP 3   Write the product.

$$-21x^5$$

SOLUTION

$$(7x^2)(-3x^3) = -21x^5$$

When you divide a monomial by a monomial, you divide the numerical coefficients and then divide the variables. If the variables are the same, you use the rule for dividing two numbers in exponent form with the same base; that is, you subtract the exponents. (See Lesson 1 if you need to review this rule.)

A fraction bar indicates division of monomials.

EXAMPLE 2

Divide: $\dfrac{-16x^4}{-8x^3}$

STRATEGY

Divide the numerical exponents and divide the variables.

STEP 1   Divide the numerical coefficients.

$$\dfrac{-16}{-8} = 2$$

STEP 2   Divide the variables.

$$\dfrac{x^4}{x^3} = x^{4-3} = x^1 = x$$

STEP 3   Write the quotient.

$$2x$$

SOLUTION

$$\dfrac{-16x^4}{-8x^3} = 2x$$

You can divide a polynomial by a monomial by dividing each term in the polynomial by the monomial.

EXAMPLE 3

Divide: $\dfrac{25x^2 - 10x + 15}{5}$

STRATEGY

Divide each term in the polynomial by 5.

STEP 1   Rewrite the fraction as a sum of fractions.

$$\frac{25x^2 - 10x + 15}{5} = \frac{25x^2}{5} + -\frac{10x}{5} + \frac{15}{5}$$

STEP 2   Compute each division.

Because the monomial 5 has no variable, you just need to divide the numerical coefficient in each term in the numerator by 5.

$$\frac{25x^2}{5} = 5x^2$$

$$\frac{-10x}{5} = -2x$$

$$\frac{15}{5} = 3$$

STEP 3   Write the quotient.

$$\frac{25x^2}{5} + -\frac{10x}{5} + \frac{15}{5} = 5x^2 + -2x + 3$$

$$= 5x^2 - 2x + 3$$

SOLUTION

$$\frac{25x^2 - 10x + 15}{5} = 5x^2 - 2x + 3$$

In the next example, you must use the rule for exponents that states that a number raised to the zero power is 1.

EXAMPLE 4   Divide: $\dfrac{27x^5 + 18x^3 - 12x^2}{-3x^2}$

STRATEGY   **Divide each term in the polynomial by $-3x^2$.**

STEP 1   Rewrite the fraction as a sum of fractions.

$$\frac{27x^5 + 18x^3 - 12x^2}{-3x^2} =$$

$$\frac{27x^5}{-3x^2} + \frac{18x^3}{-3x^2} + \frac{-12x^2}{-3x^2}$$

STEP 2   Compute each division.

Divide the numerical coefficients and divide the variables.

$$\frac{27x^5}{-3x^2} = -9x^{5-2} = -9x^3$$

$$\frac{18x^3}{-3x^2} = -6x^{3-2} = -6x^1 = -6x$$

$$\frac{-12x^2}{-3x^2} = 4x^{2-2} = 4x^0 = 4 \cdot 1 = 4$$

STEP 3   Write the quotient.

$$\frac{25x^5}{-3x^2} + \frac{18x^3}{-3x^2} + \frac{12x^3}{-3x^2}$$

$$-9x^3 + -6x + 4$$

$$-9x^3 - 6x + 4$$

SOLUTION $\dfrac{27x^5 + 18x^3 - 12x^2}{-3x^2} = -9x^3 - 6x + 4$

CHECK IT OUT with the **Coach**™

What is $24x^3 - 18x^2$ divided by $6x$?

Let's check it out.

Write the division as a single fraction. _____

Write the fraction as the sum of two fractions. _____

Compute the division indicated by each fraction. _____

What is $24x^3 - 18x^2$ divided by $6x$? _____

Sample Test Questions

1 $(2a^4)(8a^2) =$ _____

  A $16a^8$

  B $16a^6$

  C $16a^2$

  D $10a^6$

2 $(-9v^3)(-9v^3) =$ _____

  F $-81v^9$

  G $81v^9$

  H $-81v^6$

  J $81v^6$

3 $(4n^7)(-5n^8) =$ _____

  A $-20n^1$

  B $-20n^{-15}$

  C $-20n^{15}$

  D $20n^{15}$

4 $(b^4)(-2b^3) =$ _____

  F $-2b^1$

  G $-2b^7$

  H $-2b^{12}$

  J $-2b^{14}$

5 $\dfrac{36x^4}{9x^2} =$ _____

  A $27x^2$

  B $4x^2$

  C $4x^6$

  D $4x^8$

6 $\dfrac{-72n^8}{-9n^5} =$ _____

  F $8n^3$

  G $-8n^3$

  H $8n^{13}$

  J $-8n^{13}$

7 $\dfrac{28x^5 - 21x^4 + 14x^3}{7} =$ _____

  A $4x^4 - 3x^3 + 2x^2$

  B $4x^5 + 3x^4 + 2x^3$

  C $4x^5 - 3x^4 + 2x^3$

  D $21x^5 - 14x^4 + 2x^3$

8 Write the answer.

$$\frac{24a^6 - 20a^4 - 8a^2}{-4a^2} =$$ _____

Answer _____

9 Write the answer.

$$\frac{100q^{10} + 50q^6}{200q^4} =$$

Answer _____

Short-Response Question

10   The area of a rectangle is $(30x^3 + 35x^2 - 15x)$ square units and the width is $5x$ units.

What is the length of the rectangle?

Show your work.

Answer _____ units

LESSON 20

Strand 2: Algebra

Multiplying Binomials by Binomials

8.A.8 Multiply a binomial by a monomial or a binomial (integer coefficients)

You use the Distributive Property when you multiply a polynomial by a monomial.

EXAMPLE 1

Multiply: $2x(3x^2 - 14x)$

STRATEGY

Use the Distributive Property.

STEP 1   Use the Distributive Property.
$$2x(3x^2 - 14x) = (2x)(3x^2) - (2x)(14x)$$

STEP 2   Multiply each pair of monomials.
$$(2x)(3x^2) - (2x)(14x) = 6x^3 - 28x^2$$

SOLUTION

$$2x(3x^2 - 14x) = 6x^3 - 28x^2$$

When you multiply two binomials, you must multiply each term of the first binomial by each term in the second binomial. Here is a method you can use to organize your computation.

1. Multiply the **first** terms in the two binomials.

2. Multiply the **outside** terms of the binomials; that is, multiply the first term of the first binomial by the second term of the second binomial.

3. Multiply the **inside** terms of the binomials; that is, multiply the second term in the first binomial by the first term in the second binomial.

4. Multiply the **last** terms in the two binomials.

5. If any of the products are like terms, combine them.

You may know a name for the method above. The name uses the first letter of each of the bold-faced words above: **FOIL**.

EXAMPLE 2

Multiply: $(4x + 6)(3x + 7)$

STRATEGY

Use the FOIL method.

STEP 1 Multiply the **first** terms of the two binomials to get a partial product.

$(\mathbf{4x} + 6)(\mathbf{3x} + 7) = \mathbf{12x^2} + \ldots$

STEP 2 Multiply the **outside** terms to get the next partial product.

$(\mathbf{4x} + 6)(3x + \mathbf{7}) = 12x^2 + \mathbf{28x} + \ldots$

STEP 3 Multiply the **inside** terms.

$(4x + \mathbf{6})(\mathbf{3x} + 7) = 12x^2 + 28x + \mathbf{18x} + \ldots$

STEP 4 Multiply the **last** terms.

$(4x + \mathbf{6})(3x + \mathbf{7}) = 12x^2 + 28x + 18x + \mathbf{42}$

STEP 5 Combine like terms.

In $12x^2 + 28x + 18x + 42$, the terms $28x$ and $18x$ are like terms. Combine them by adding their numerical coefficients.

$12x^2 + 28x + 18x + 42 = 12x^2 + 46x + 42$

SOLUTION

$\mathbf{(4x + 6)(3x + 7) = 12x^2 + 46x + 42}$

Be careful with signs when one or both of the binomials involve subtraction.

EXAMPLE 3

Simplify: $(3x - 2)^2$

STRATEGY

Use the meaning of squaring a quantity. Then use FOIL.

STEP 1 Show the squared binomial as the product of two binomials.

The base of the exponent expression is the binomial $3x - 2$.

$(3x - 2)^2 = (3x - 2)(3x - 2)$

STEP 2 Use FOIL.

Notice that both binomials show subtraction.

$(3x - 2)(3x - 2) = 9x^2 - 6x - 6x + 4$

STEP 3 Combine like terms.

$9x^2 - 6x - 6x + 4 = 9x^2 - 12x + 4$

SOLUTION

$\mathbf{(3x - 2)^2 = 9x^2 - 12x + 4}$

CHECK IT OUT *with the* **Coach**™

How can you find the product $(4x + 2)(8x + 1)$?

Let's check it out.

The product of the first terms is _____.

The product of the outside terms is _____.

The product of the inside terms is _____.

The product of the last terms is _____.

$(4x + 2)(8x + 1) = $ _____

Sample Test Questions

1 $3n(n^2 - 64) = $ _____

   A $3n^2 + 192$

   B $3n^3 - 192$

   C $3n^3 - 192n$

   D $3n^3 - 192n^2$

2 $(-5n^2)(2n^3 - 6n) = $ _____

   F $10n^2 - 30n$

   G $10n^5 + 30n^3$

   H $-10n^6 + 30n^3$

   J $-10n^5 + 30n^3$

3 $(t + 7)(t + 3) = $ _____

   A $t^2 + 10t + 21$

   B $t^2 + 4t + 10$

   C $t^2 + 21t + 10$

   D $t^2 + 3t + 21$

4 $(n + 5)(4n + 9) = $ _____

   F $4n^2 + 11n + 45$

   G $4n^2 + 29n + 45$

   H $4n^2 + 29n + 14$

   J $5n^2 + 29n + 45$

5 $(3a - 6)(8a + 2) = $ _____

   A $24a^2 + 42a + 12$

   B $24a^2 - 42a + 12$

   C $24a^2 - 42a - 12$

   D $24a^2 - 54a - 12$

6 $(n - 9)(2n - 4) = $ _____

   F $2n^2 - 22n + 36$

   G $2n^2 - 22n - 36$

   H $2n^2 + 22n + 36$

   J $2n^2 + 22n - 36$

7 $(x + 10)(x - 10) = $ _____

A $x^2 + 20x - 100$

B $x^2 - 20x - 100$

C $x^2 + 100$

D $x^2 - 100$

8 Write the answer.

$(5x + 2)^2 = $ _____

Answer _____

9 Write the answer.

$(8Q - 4)(5Q + 10) = $ _____

Answer _____

Short-Response Question

10 A rectangle has a length of $(6x + 1)$ units and a width of $(3x + 1)$ units.

Part A

Write a trinomial that represents the area of the rectangle.

Answer _____ square units

Part B

Explain how you determined your answer to Part A.

_____

_____

_____

_____

Strand 2: Algebra

Introduction to Factoring

8.A.10 Factor algebraic expressions using the GCF

When you find the greatest common factor (GCF) of two numbers, you find the greatest number that divides both of the numbers. For example, the GCF of 18 and 24 is 6 because 6 is the greatest number that divides both 18 and 24.

When you find the greatest common factor of two algebraic expressions involving variables, you find the greatest variable expression that divides both of the given expressions. For example, the GCF of x^5 and x^3 is x^3 because x^3 is the greatest variable expression that divides both x^5 and x^3. (Note: x and x^2 are also common factors of x^5 and x^3, but x^3 is the greatest common factor since it has the greatest exponent.)

When finding the GCF of a polynomial expression, you find the greatest monomial that divides all the terms in the polynomial. Then you write the polynomial in factored form by showing the product of the GCF and the quotient you got from dividing the given polynomial by the GCF.

EXAMPLE 1

Factor: $3x + 6y$

STRATEGY

Find the greatest monomial that divides the terms of the polynomial.

STEP 1   Find the GCF of the numerical coefficients.

The GCF of 3 and 6 is 3.

STEP 2   Find the GCF of the variables in the terms.

The terms have different variables, so there are no variables in common.

STEP 3   Divide the polynomial by the GCF.

$\frac{3x + 6y}{3} = \frac{3x}{3} + \frac{6y}{3} = x + 2y$

STEP 4   Write the given polynomial as the product of the GCF and the polynomial that results from dividing the given polynomial by the GCF.

GCF × (quotient of given polynomial and the GCF)

$3 \times (x + 2y)$

SOLUTION

$3x + 6y = 3(x + 2y)$

EXAMPLE 2

Factor: $24z^2 - 32z$

STRATEGY

Find the greatest monomial that divides the terms of the polynomial.

STEP 1 Find the GCF of the numerical coefficients.

The GCF of 24 and 32 is 8.

STEP 2 Find the GCF of the variables in the terms.

The GCF of z^2 and z is z.

So, the monomial that is the GCF of $24z^2 - 32z$ is $8 \cdot z$, or $8z$.

STEP 3 Divide the polynomial by the GCF monomial.

$$\frac{24z^2 - 32z}{8z} = \frac{24z^2}{8z} - \frac{32z}{8z}$$
$$= 3z - 4$$

STEP 4 Write the given polynomial as the product of the GCF and the polynomial that results from dividing the given polynomial by the GCF.

GCF $\times$ (quotient of given polynomial and the GCF)

$8z \times (3z - 4)$

SOLUTION **$24z^2 - 32z = 8z(3z - 4)$**

EXAMPLE 3

Factor: $14x^4 - 35x^3 + 7x^2$

STRATEGY

Find the greatest monomial that divides the terms of the polynomial.

STEP 1 Find the GCF of the numerical coefficients.

The GCF of 14, 35, and 7 is 7.

STEP 2 Find the GCF of the variables in the terms.

The GCF of x^4, x^3, and x^2 is x^2.

So, the monomial that is the GCF of $14x^4 - 35x^3 + 7x^2$ is $7x^2$.

STEP 3 Divide the polynomial by the GCF monomial.

$$\frac{14x^4 - 35x^3 + 7x^2}{7x^2} = \frac{14x^4}{7x^2} - \frac{35x^3}{7x^2} + \frac{7x^2}{7x^2}$$
$$= 2x^2 - 5x + 1$$

STEP 4 Write the given polynomial as the product of the GCF and the polynomial that results from dividing the given polynomial by the GCF.

GCF $\times$ (quotient of given polynomial and the GCF)

$7x^2 \times (2x^2 - 5x + 1)$

SOLUTION **$14x^4 - 35x^3 + 7x^2 = 7x^2 \times (2x^2 - 5x + 1)$**

Note: You can check your answers by working backward. That is, you can apply the Distributive Property to the factored form and check to see if you get the original polynomial. For Example 3:

$$7x^2 \times (2x^2 - 5x + 1) = (7x^2)(2x^2) - (7x^2)(5x) + (7x^2)(1)$$
$$= 14x^4 - 35x^3 + 7x^2$$

CHECK IT OUT with the Coach

How can you write the polynomial $12x^3 + 24x^2 - 36x$ as a product of its greatest common factor and a polynomial?

Let's check it out.

The GCF of the numerical coefficients is _____.

The GCF of the variables in the terms is _____.

The GCF monomial is _____.

The quotient of the given polynomial and the GCF monomial is _____.

$12x^3 + 24x^2 - 36x$ as a product of its greatest common factor and a polynomial is _____.

Sample Test Questions

For Questions 1–7, choose the answer that shows the given polynomial as the product of its GCF and a polynomial.

1 $4a + 6b =$ _____

  A $2a(2 + 3b)$

  B $2b(2a + 3)$

  C $2(2a + 3b)$

  D $2(8a + 12b)$

2 $11t - 22 =$ _____

  F $11(t + 2)$

  G $11(t - 2)$

  H $t(11 - 22)$

  J $11t(t - 2)$

3 $4x^2 - 36x =$ _____

  A $2x(x^2 - 18)$

  B $4(x^2 - 9x)$

  C $x(4x - 36)$

  D $4x(x - 9)$

4 $25r^3 - 75r =$ _____

  F $25r(r^2 - 3)$

  G $25(r^3 - 3r)$

  H $5(5r^2 - 15r)$

  J $5r(5r^2 - 15)$

5 $9y^4 - 3y^2 =$ _____

    A $3(3y^4 - y^2)$

    B $3y(3y^3 - y)$

    C $3y^2(3y^2 - 3)$

    D $3y^2(3y^2 - 1)$

6 $ab^2 + a^2b =$ _____

    F $a(b^2 + ab)$

    G $b(ab + a^2)$

    H $ab(b + a)$

    J $ab(b^2 + a^2)$

7 $5x^2 - 10x + 20 =$ _____

    A $5(x^2 - 10x + 20)$

    B $5(x^2 - 2x + 4)$

    C $5(x^2 - 5x + 15)$

    D $5x(x - 2x + 4)$

8 Write the answer that shows the given polynomial as the product of its GCF and a polynomial.

$$24d^4 - 36d^3 + 18d^2 =$$ _____

Answer _____

9 Write the answer that shows the given polynomial as the product of its GCF and a polynomial.

$$13T^6 - 39T^2 =$$ _____

Answer _____

Short-Response Question

10 Write the polynomial below as the product of its GCF and a polynomial.

$$27x^3 + 27x^2 - 9x$$

Show your work.

Answer _____

LESSON 22

Strand 2: Algebra

Factoring Trinomials

8.A.11 Factor a trinomial in the form $ax^2 + bx + c$; $a = 1$ and c having no more than 3 sets of factors

In Lesson 20, you saw how the product of two binomials can be a trinomial. In this lesson you will work backward from what you learned in Lesson 20. That is, you will start with a trinomial and write it in factored form as a product of two binomials.

Remember the FOIL method for multiplying binomials. It will help you to factor trinomials.

EXAMPLE 1

Factor: $x^2 + 5x + 6$

STRATEGY

Think of how the FOIL method is used to write the product of binomials as a trinomial.

STEP 1   Factor the first term in the trinomial.

$x^2 = x \cdot x$, so x goes into the first position in each binomial.

$(? + ?)(? + ?) = (x + ?)(x + ?)$

STEP 2   Factor the third term in the trinomial.

$6 = 1 \cdot 6$, and $6 = 2 \cdot 3$, so there are two choices for the second position in the binomials: 1 and 6, and 2 and 3.

So $(x + ?)(x + ?) = (x + 1)(x + 6)$
or $(x + ?)(x + ?) = (x + 2)(x + 3)$

STEP 3   Find the factors of the third term that have a sum equal to the numerical coefficient of the middle term.

$1 + 6 = 7$

$2 + 3 = 5$

2 and 3 are the factors that have a sum of 5, so 2 and 3 go into the second positions of the binomials.

$(x + 2)(x + 3)$

SOLUTION

$x^2 + 5x + 6 = (x + 2)(x + 3)$

Note: You can check your work by working backward. Multiply the binomials to see if you get the given trinomial for a product.

The sign of the middle term of the trinomial can help you to decide how to factor the third term of the trinomial.

EXAMPLE 2

Factor: $x^2 - 5x + 4$

STRATEGY

Think of how the FOIL method is used to write the product of binomials as a trinomial.

STEP 1   Factor the first term in the trinomial.

$x^2 = x \cdot x$, so x goes into the first position in each binomial.

$(? + ?)(? + ?) = (x + ?)(x + ?)$

STEP 2   Factor the third term in the trinomial.

The third term is positive 4. But notice that the middle term is a subtraction, so think of the numerical coefficient of the middle term as -5.

You need to find two numbers whose product is positive 4 but whose sum is negative 5. That means that both factors of 4 must be negative. The possibilities for the second position in the binomials are: -2 and -2, and -1 and -4.

So $(x + ?)(x + ?) = (x + (-2))(x + (-2))$
or $(x + ?)(x + ?) = (x + (-1))(x + (-4))$

STEP 3   Find the factors of the third term that have a sum equal to the numerical coefficient of the middle term.

$-2 + -2 = -4$

$-1 + -4 = -5$

-1 and -4 are the factors of positive 4 that have a sum of -5, so -1 and -4 go into the second positions of the binomials.

$(x + (-1))(x + (-4)) = (x - 1)(x - 4)$

SOLUTION

$x^2 - 5x + 4 = (x - 1)(x - 4)$

Check your answer by multiplying the binomials.

EXAMPLE 3

Factor: $x^2 - 2x - 3$

STRATEGY

Think of how the FOIL method is used to write the product of binomials as a trinomial.

STEP 1 Factor the first term in the trinomial.

$x^2 = x \cdot x$, so x goes into the first position in each binomial.

$(? + ?)(? + ?) = (x + ?)(x + ?)$

STEP 2 Factor the third term in the trinomial.

The third term is -3. So one of the factors must be negative and the other positive.

You need to find two numbers whose product is negative 3 and whose sum is negative 2. The possibilities for the second position in the binomials are: 1 and -3, and -1 and 3.

So $(x + ?)(x + ?) = (x + 1)(x + (-3))$
or $(x + ?)(x + ?) = (x + (-1))(x + 3)$

STEP 3 Find the factors of the third term that have a sum equal to the numerical coefficient of the middle term.

$1 + -3 = -2$

$-1 + 3 = 2$

1 and -3 are the factors of -3 that have a sum of -2, so 1 and -3 go into the second positions of the binomials.

$(x + 1)(x + (-3)) = (x + 1)(x - 3)$

SOLUTION

$x^2 - 2x - 3 = (x + 1)(x - 3)$

CHECK IT OUT with the Coach™

What is $x^2 + 14x + 13$ in factored form?

Let's check it out.

The factors of the first term of the trinomial are _____.

The factors of the third term of the trinomial are _____.

The factors of 13 that have a sum of 14 are _____.

In factored form, $x^2 + 14x + 13 =$ _____.

Sample Test Questions

For Questions 1–7, find the factored form of each trinomial.

1 $a^2 + 8a + 7 =$ _____

    A $(a + 7)(a + 1)$

    B $(a - 7)(a - 1)$

    C $(a + 7)(a - 1)$

    D $(a - 7)(a + 1)$

2 $m^2 + 7m + 10 =$ _____

    F $(m + 1)(m + 10)$

    G $(m + 2)(m + 5)$

    H $(m + 3)(m + 7)$

    J $(m - 2)(m - 5)$

3 $x^2 - 6x + 9 =$ _____

    A $(x + 3)^2$

    B $(x - 1)(x - 9)$

    C $(x - 3)^2$

    D $(x - 3)(x + 3)$

4 $x^2 + 2x - 3 =$ _____

    F $(x - 3)(x + 1)$

    G $(x + 3)(x + 1)$

    H $(x - 1)(x - 3)$

    J $(x - 1)(x + 3)$

5 $x^2 - 6x + 5 =$ _____

    A $(x - 1)(x - 5)$

    B $(x - 1)(x + 5)$

    C $(x + 1)(x - 5)$

    D $(x + 1)(x + 5)$

6 $n^2 - 2n + 1 =$ _____

    F $(n - 1)(n + 1)$

    G $(n - 1)(n - 1)$

    H $(n - 2)(n + 1)$

    J $(n + 2)(n - 1)$

7 $y^2 + y - 2 =$ _____

    A $(y - 1)(y + 2)$

    B $(y - 2)(y + 1)$

    C $(y - 1)(y - 1)$

    D $(y - 2)(y - 1)$

8   Write the factored form of this trinomial.

$$d^2 + 6d + 8 = \underline{\hspace{2cm}}$$

Answer _____

9   Write the factored form of this trinomial.

$$M^2 - 7M + 10 = \underline{\hspace{2cm}}$$

Answer _____

Extended-Response Question

10

Part A

Factor this trinomial: $x^2 - 8x + 15$

Answer _____

Part B

Explain the steps you took to find your answer in Part A.

_____

_____

_____

Part C

How can you check your answer in Part A?

_____

_____

_____

LESSON 23

Strand 2: Algebra

Understanding Representations of Numerical Information

8.A.15 Understand that numerical information can be represented in multiple ways: arithmetically, algebraically, and graphically

Numerical information is often presented in various ways in the context of solving problems. Some ways of presentation lead to more efficient problem solving. Three common ways to present numerical information are: numerical, algebraic, and graphical.

EXAMPLE 1

The XYZ Dry Cleaning store charges a flat fee of $2.00 per order plus x per shirt, depending on the fabric. In what form is the information in the problem presented?

STRATEGY

Look at the information in the problem.

The problem presents the information with numbers and variables. Because variables are included, an algebraic presentation method is used.

SOLUTION

The information in the problem is presented algebraically.

EXAMPLE 2

Suppose the XYZ Dry Cleaning store was considering a fixed price for the price per shirt. The manager decided to charge $1.50 per shirt. In what form is this information now provided?

STRATEGY

Look at how the information in the problem changed.

The problem was changed so that all information is in the form of fixed numbers.

SOLUTION

The information in the problem is presented arithmetically.

How could the XYZ Dry Cleaning manager show the numerical information graphically?

Let's check it out.

What would the manager plot along the horizontal axis? _____

What would the manager plot along the vertical axis? _____

So the manager could show a graph of _____ vs. _____.

Sample Test Questions

1 Iris surveyed her classmates on the number of hours each spends on homework. She decides to display her data with a circle graph. How has she chosen to present her data?

   A arithmetically

   B algebraically

   C graphically

   D none of the above

2 Arthur knows the number of points he scores in a game is represented by $4b$, where b is the number of baskets he scores. How are Arthur's points represented?

   F arithmetically

   G algebraically

   H graphically

   J none of the above

3 A tow truck company uses the expression $\$25 + \$9m$ to determine the cost of towing, where m is the number of miles towed. Which information in the problem is presented as algebraic information?

   A $25, which represents the flat fee

   B $9, which represents the cost per mile

   C m, which represents the number of miles towed

   D There is no algebraic information in the problem.

4 Which information below is best presented graphically?

   F A golfer's score after 1 round.

   G The number of strokes a golfer needs to score in order to place first in a tournament.

   H A golfer's best score.

   J A golfer's scores over a period of five years.

5 Which expression is presented arithmetically?

   A $(x + 9) \times 15$ **C** $\frac{8}{9} + 19$

   B $17 - y + 81$ **D** $16.7n \div 14$

6 The same data is presented below in three different forms. Draw lines to match the appropriate form to the type of information provided.

algebraic   graphical   numerical

$y = 0.9x + 3$

x	y
0	3
1	3.9
2	4.8
3	5.7

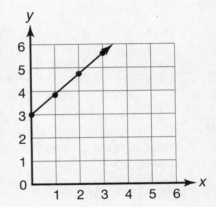

Short-Response Question

7 There are three common forms used to show information in a problem.

Part A

Explain the difference between a numerical presentation of information and an algebraic presentation of information.

_____

_____

Part B

Give two examples of how to show information presented in a graphical form.

_____

_____

Progress Check for Lessons 15–23

1 In this expression, the variable *m* represents the number of dollars in Gerald's bank account.

$3m + 20$

Which verbal expression matches the expression?

A three times the sum of the dollars in Gerald's account and twenty dollars

B twenty dollars more than three times the number of dollars in Gerald's account

C three dollars more than twenty times the number of dollars in Gerald's account

D the product of three times the number of dollars in Gerald's account and 20 dollars

2 So far this year, the school has raised $550 for its scholarship program. There are 4 more days remaining in the campaign to raise funds for the program. Which inequality can be used to find *n*, the average amount of money that the school must raise each day in order to exceed the $850 that was raised last year?

F $4n + 550 > 850$

G $4n - 550 > 850$

H $4(n - 550) > 850$

J $550 - 4n > 850$

3 Which situation matches this graph?

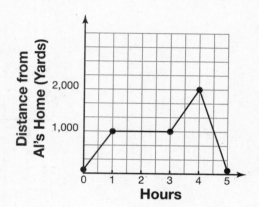

A Al walked to his friend's house and stayed for 2 hours, and then walked home.

B Al walked to his friend's house and stayed for 1 hour, walked to his cousin's house, and then walked home.

C Al walked to his friend's house and stayed for 2 hours, then walked to his cousin's house, and then jogged home.

D Al ran to his friend's house and stayed for 2 hours, then walked to his cousin's house and stayed there.

4 Michelle bought a plant that was 4 inches tall. The plant grew at the rate of 2 inches per week. Which graph shows this situation?

F

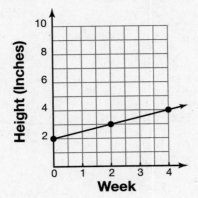

H

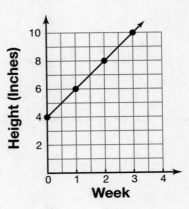

G

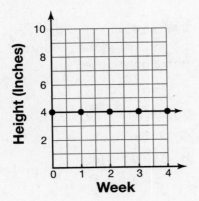

J

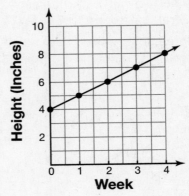

5 Which equation has this graph?

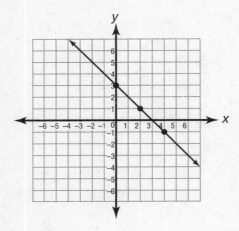

- **A** $y = x + 3$
- **B** $y = x - 3$
- **C** $y = -3x$
- **D** $y = -x + 3$

6 $(5x^2 - 3x - 2) + (x^2 - 4x + 4) = $ _____

- **F** $6x^2 - 7x + 2$
- **G** $6x^2 + 7x - 2$
- **H** $6x^2 - 7x - 6$
- **J** $5x^2 - 7x + 2$

7 $(-3x^3)(-9x^2) = $ _____

- **A** $12x^6$
- **B** $27x^6$
- **C** $27x^5$
- **D** $-27x^5$

8 $\dfrac{54x^5 - 36x^3 + 9x^2}{}$ = _____

- **F** $-6x^3 + 4x - 1$
- **G** $-6x^3 + 4x + 1$
- **H** $-6x^3 - 4x - 1$
- **J** $-6x^3 - 4x + 1$

9 $(6x + 5)(2x - 1) = $ _____

- **A** $12x^2 - 4x - 5$
- **B** $12x^2 + 4x - 5$
- **C** $12x^2 + 4x + 5$
- **D** $12x^2 + 16x - 5$

10 Which of the following shows this polynomial as the product of its GCF and a polynomial?

$$64n^3 - 48n$$

- **F** $4n(16n^2 - 12)$
- **G** $8n(8n^2 - 6)$
- **H** $16(4n^3 - 3n)$
- **J** $16n(4n^2 - 3)$

11 Factor: $x^2 + 4x - 5$

A $(x + 5)(x + 1)$

B $(x - 5)(x - 1)$

C $(x + 5)(x - 1)$

D $(x - 5)(x + 1)$

12 A car service charges a flat fee of $6 and $5 per mile or part of a mile. Which of the following could you use to find the cost of a 7-mile ride?

F $7 \cdot 6 + 5$

G $7 \cdot 5 + 6$

H $7(6 + 5)$

J $7 \cdot 5 - 6$

Open-Ended Questions

Short-Response Question

13 Simplify the following polynomial.

$(3x - 4)(x + 6) - 2x^2 + 2(x - 1)$

Show your work.

Answer _____

Short-Response Question

14 This is a rectangle model for the product of two binomials. In the model, each small square represents 1, each rectangle represents x, and the large square represents x^2.

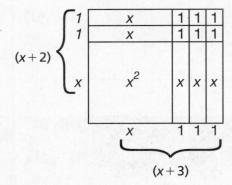

The area of the rectangle is the product of the length and width. The length of the rectangle above is $x + 3$ and the width is $x + 2$. The rectangle is made up of 1 large square plus 5 rectangles plus 6 small squares, which is $x^2 + 5x + 6$, which is the product you would get if you multiplied the binomials $x + 3$ and $x + 2$.

Part A

Which two binomials would give the product shown in the model below?

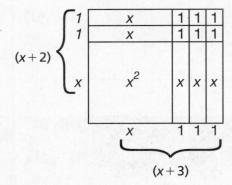

Answer _____

Part B

What is the product shown in the model above?

Answer _____

Extended-Response Question

15   On a game show, Paul has 4 less points than twice the number of points Dan has.

Part A

Complete the table to find some ordered pairs that are part of the relationship.

x	y = 2x − 4	y	(x,y)
−1			
0			
1			
3			

Part B

Plot your ordered pairs on the coordinate grid below, and draw a line through the points.

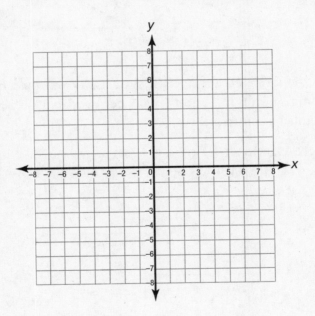

Part C

What if the situation were changed to Paul has twice as many points as Dan. How would the graph compare to the graph you completed in Part B?

_____

_____

LESSON 24

Special Angles

8.G.1 Identify pairs of vertical angles as congruent

8.G.2 Identify pairs of supplementary and complementary angles

8.G.3 Calculate the missing angle in a supplementary or complementary pair

8.G.6 Calculate the missing angle measurements when given two intersecting lines and an angle

ADJACENT ANGLES

Adjacent angles are angles that have a common side and do not overlap.

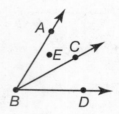

In the figure above, $\angle ABC$ and $\angle CBD$ are adjacent angles. They have common side $\overrightarrow{BC}$, and they do not overlap. That is, they have no interior points in common.

$\angle ABC$ and $\angle ABD$ are not adjacent angles. They have common side $\overrightarrow{BA}$ but they overlap. That is, point E in the interior of $\angle ABC$ is also in the interior of $\angle ABD$.

SUPPLEMENTARY AND COMPLEMENTARY ANGLES

Two angles are **supplementary angles** if the sum of their measures is 180°.

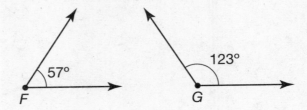

Since 57° + 123° = 180°, ∠F is supplementary to ∠G.

If non-common sides of two adjacent angles form a straight line, then the angles are supplementary.

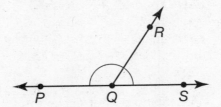

∠PQR and ∠RQS are supplementary angles.

Two angles are **complementary angles** if the sum of their measures is 90°.

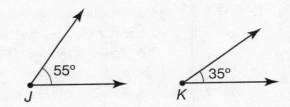

Since 55° + 35° = 90°, ∠J is complementary to ∠K.

If the non-common sides of two adjacent angles are perpendicular, then the angles are complementary.

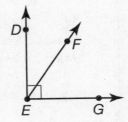

Since $\overrightarrow{ED}$ is perpendicular to $\overrightarrow{EG}$, the measure of ∠DEG is 90°.
So ∠DEF and ∠FEG are complementary angles.

VERTICAL ANGLES

Vertical angles are two nonadjacent angles formed when two lines intersect. In the figure below lines AC and BD intersect at point P.

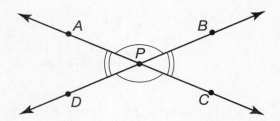

$\angle APB$ and $\angle DPC$ are vertical angles.

$\angle APD$ and $\angle BPC$ are vertical angles.

Vertical angles are congruent, so in the figure above, m$\angle APB$ = m$\angle DPC$, and m$\angle APD$ = m$\angle BPC$.

EXAMPLE 1

Lines m and n intersect to form angles 1, 2, 3, and 4. If the m$\angle 1$ = 36°, what is m$\angle 2$? m$\angle 3$? m$\angle 4$?

STRATEGY   **Use information about the types of angles presented in this lesson.**

STEP 1   Use the definition of vertical angles.

$\angle 1$ and $\angle 3$ are vertical angles because they are nonadjacent angles formed by two intersecting lines.

Therefore, m$\angle 3$ = m$\angle 1$ = 36°.

STEP 2   Look at the non-common sides of adjacent angles 1 and 2.

The non-common sides of these angles form a straight line. Therefore, $\angle 1$ and $\angle 2$ are supplementary angles.

$$m\angle 1 + m\angle 2 = 180°$$
$$36° + m\angle 2 = 180°$$
$$m\angle 2 = 180° - 36° = 144°$$

STEP 3   Use the definition of vertical angles again.

$\angle 2$ and $\angle 4$ are vertical angles because they are nonadjacent angles formed by two intersecting lines. Vertical angles are congruent. From Step 2, you know that m$\angle 2$ = 144°.

Therefore, m$\angle 4$ = m$\angle 2$ = 144°.

SOLUTION   **m$\angle 2$ = 144°; m$\angle 3$ = 36°; m$\angle 4$ = 144°**

EXAMPLE 2

In this figure, lines *AB* and *FE* intersect at point *C*. Ray *CD* is perpendicular to line *AB*.

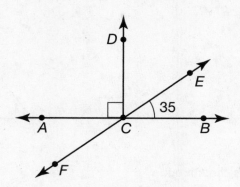

1) What is the measure of ∠*ACE*?

2) What is the measure of ∠*ACF*?

3) What is the measure of ∠*DCE*?

STRATEGY   **Use information about angle pairs presented in this lesson.**

STEP 1   Find the measure of ∠*ACE*.

∠*ACE* is adjacent to ∠*ECB*, and their non-common sides form a straight line. So, ∠*ACE* and ∠*ECB* are supplementary angles.

Find the measure of ∠*DCE* by subtracting the measure of ∠*ECB* from 180°:

m∠*ACE* = 180° − m∠*ECB*

= 180° − 35°

= 145°

STEP 2   Find the measure of ∠*ACF*.

∠*ACF* and ∠*ECB* are vertical angles. Since vertical angles are congruent, m∠*ACF* = m∠*ECB* = 35°.

STEP 3   Find the measure of ∠*DCE*.

∠*DCE* is adjacent to ∠*ECB*, and their non-common sides are perpendicular. So, ∠*DCE* and ∠*ECB* are complementary angles.

Find the measure of ∠*DCE* by subtracting the measure of ∠*ECB* from 90°:

m∠*DCE* = 90° − m∠*ECB*

= 90° − 35°

= 55°

SOLUTION   1) m∠*ACE* = 145°; 2) m∠*ACF* = 35°; 3) m∠*DCE* = 55°.

This figure shows $\overleftrightarrow{RS}$ and $\overrightarrow{TV}$. The measure of ∠VTS is 52°. What is the measure of ∠RTV?

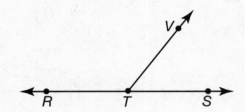

Let's check it out.

∠RTV and ∠VTS have a common _____ and no _____ in common.

Therefore, ∠RTV and ∠VTS are _____ angles.

The non-common sides of ∠RTV and ∠VTS form a _____.

Therefore, ∠RTV and ∠VTS are _____ angles.

m∠RTV + m∠VTS = _____

So, m∠RTV = _____° − _____° = _____°.

Sample Test Questions

1 If ∠PQR is supplementary to ∠RQS and m∠RQS = 110°, what is the measure of ∠PQR?

A 50°

B 60°

C 70°

D 80°

2 If ∠A is complementary to ∠B and m∠A = 48°, what is the measure of ∠B?

F 32°

G 42°

H 132°

J 142°

3 If ∠AXD and ∠CXB are vertical angles and m∠CXB = 30°, what is the measure of ∠AXD?

A 30°

B 60°

C 90°

D 150°

4 Lines *RS* and *TV* intersect to form angles 1, 2, 3, and 4. The measure of ∠2 = 130°

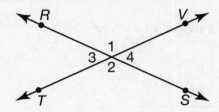

What are the measures of the other angles?

F m∠1 = 130°; m∠3 = 130°; m∠4 = 130°

G m∠1 = 50°; m∠3 = 50°; m∠4 = 130°

H m∠1 = 130°; m∠3 = 50°; m∠4 = 50°

J m∠1 = 130°; m∠3 = 60°; m∠4 = 60°

In the figure below, lines *FH* and *GJ* intersect at point *P*. Ray *PK* is perpendicular to line *FH*. Use this figure to answer Questions 5–9.

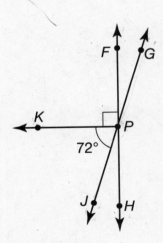

5 Which is a pair of supplementary angles?

A ∠JPK and ∠JPH

B ∠GPH and ∠JPH

C ∠FPG and ∠KPH

D ∠JPH and ∠FPG

6 Which is a pair of complementary angles?

F ∠FPG and ∠JPH

G ∠KPJ and ∠KPF

H ∠KPJ and ∠JPH

J ∠KPH and ∠KPF

7 What is the measure of ∠KPG?

A 18°

B 72°

C 90°

D 108°

8 What is the measure of ∠JPH?

F 8°

G 18°

H 28°

J 38°

9 What is the measure of ∠FPG? Write the answer.

Answer _____

Short-Response Question

10   If two vertical angles are complementary, what is the measure of each angle? Explain your answer.

_____

_____

_____

_____

Strand 3: Geometry

Angles Formed by Parallel Lines and a Transversal

8.G.4 Determine angle pair relationship when given two parallel lines cut by a transversal

8.G.5 Calculate the missing angle measurements when given two parallel lines cut by a transversal

When two **parallel lines** are cut by a third line, some special angle pairs are formed.

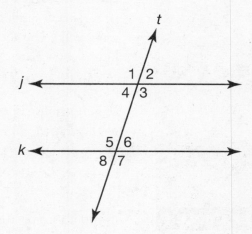

In the figure above, lines *j* and *k* are parallel and are intersected by line *t*. This intersecting line is called a **transversal**. You should know these special angle pairs formed and their relationship:

Alternate interior angles: A pair of nonadjacent angles, both inside the parallel lines, on opposite (alternate) sides of the transversal. The alternate interior angles above are:

∠3 and ∠5   ∠4 and ∠6

When parallel lines are cut by a transversal, alternate interior angles are congruent, so

∠3 ≅ ∠5 and ∠4 ≅ ∠6.

Corresponding angles: A pair of nonadjacent angles—one inside the parallel lines and one outside the parallel lines—that are both on the same side of the transversal. The corresponding angles above are:

∠1 and ∠5   ∠2 and ∠6
∠3 and ∠7   ∠4 and ∠8

When parallel lines are cut by a transversal, corresponding angles are congruent, so

∠1 ≅ ∠5, ∠2 ≅ ∠6, ∠3 ≅ ∠7, and ∠4 ≅ ∠8.

Alternate exterior angles: A pair of nonadjacent angles, both outside the parallel lines, on opposite sides of the transversal. The alternate exterior angles above are:

$\angle 1$ and $\angle 7$ $\angle 2$ and $\angle 8$

When parallel lines are cut by a transversal, alternate exterior angles are congruent, so

$\angle 1 \cong \angle 7$ and $\angle 2 \cong \angle 8$.

Interior angles on the same side of the transversal: A pair of nonadjacent angles, both inside the parallel lines, on the same side of the transversal. The interior angles on the same side of the transversal in the figure above are:

$\angle 3$ and $\angle 6$ $\angle 4$ and $\angle 5$

When parallel lines are cut by a transversal, interior angles on the same side of the transversal are supplementary, so

$m\angle 3 + m\angle 6 = 180°$ and
$m\angle 4 + m\angle 5 = 180°$.

EXAMPLE 1

In the figure on the right, lines p and q are parallel. The measure of $\angle 3 = 126°$. What is the measure of $\angle 6$?

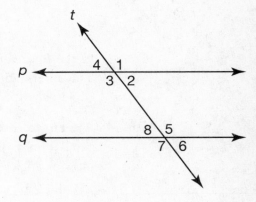

STRATEGY

Use the relationships of angles formed when parallel lines are cut by a transversal.

STEP 1   How are $\angle 3$ and $\angle 6$ related?

$\angle 3$ and $\angle 6$ are not a special angle pair.

However, $\angle 3$ and $\angle 5$ are alternate interior angles; and $\angle 5$ and $\angle 6$ are supplementary angles. Use this information to find the measure of $\angle 6$.

STEP 2   What is the measure of $\angle 5$?

$\angle 3$ and $\angle 5$ are alternate interior angles.

So $m\angle 5 = m\angle 3 = 126°$.

STEP 3   What is the measure of $\angle 6$?

$\angle 5$ and $\angle 6$ are supplementary, so $m\angle 6 + m\angle 5 = 180°$.

$m\angle 6 = 180° - m\angle 5 = 180° - 126° = 54°$

SOLUTION   **$m\angle 6 = 54°$**

There are many ways to solve problems such as the one in Example 1. Example 2 shows another way to solve the same problem.

EXAMPLE 2

In the figure below, lines *p* and *q* are parallel. The measure of ∠3 = 126°. What is the measure of ∠6?

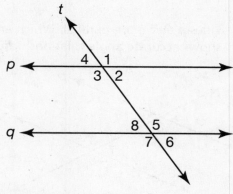

STRATEGY

Use the relationships of angles formed when parallel lines are cut by a transversal.

STEP 1   Find another way to relate ∠6 to ∠3.

∠3 and ∠8 are a pair of interior angles on the same side of the transversal. ∠8 and ∠6 are vertical angles. Use this information to find the measure of ∠6.

STEP 2   Find the measure of ∠8.

∠8 and ∠3 are interior angles on the same side of the transversal, so they are supplementary.

m∠8 + m∠3 = 180°

m∠8 = 180 − m∠3 = 180° − 126° = 54°

STEP 3   Find the measure of ∠6.

∠6 and ∠8 are vertical angles, so m∠6 = m∠8 = 54°.

SOLUTION   **m∠6 = 54°**

Lines *a* and *b* are parallel, and line *c* is a transversal. If m∠4 = 72°, what is the measure of ∠8?

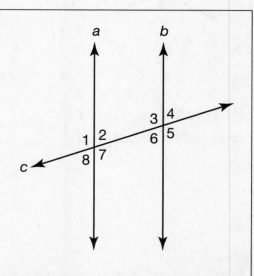

Let's check it out.

∠4 and ∠8 are a pair of _____ angles.

Therefore, m∠4 and m∠8 are _____.

m∠8 = _____

Sample Test Questions

1 Lines *p* and *q* are parallel. Which answer shows accurate angle relationships?

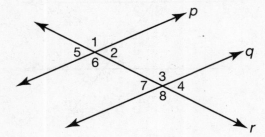

A ∠1 ≅ ∠3; ∠6 ≅ ∠7

B ∠1 ≅ ∠3; ∠6 ≅ ∠8

C ∠3 ≅ ∠5; ∠1 ≅ ∠8

D ∠5 ≅ ∠7; ∠2 ≅ ∠3

2 Lines *m* and *n* are parallel. Which answer shows accurate angle relationships?

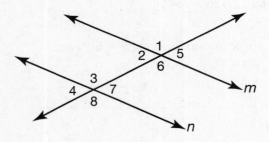

F ∠6 ≅ ∠7; ∠2 ≅ ∠7

G ∠3 ≅ ∠6; ∠2 ≅ ∠3

H ∠3 ≅ ∠6; ∠2 ≅ ∠8

J ∠3 ≅ ∠6; ∠2 ≅ ∠7

3 Lines *r* and *s* are parallel. Which answer shows accurate angle relationships?

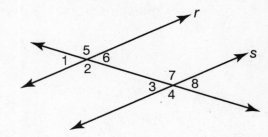

A ∠4 ≅ ∠5; ∠1 ≅ ∠8

B ∠4 ≅ ∠5; ∠2 ≅ ∠8

C ∠4 ≅ ∠6; ∠4 ≅ ∠5

D ∠5 ≅ ∠7; ∠1 ≅ ∠7

4 Lines *j* and *k* are parallel. Which answer shows an accurate angle relationship?

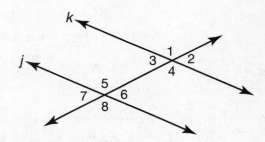

F ∠3 is supplementary to ∠6.

G ∠3 is supplementary to ∠7.

H ∠3 is supplementary to ∠5.

J ∠3 is supplementary to ∠2.

5 Lines n_1 and n_2 are parallel.
If m∠8 = 65°, what is the measure of ∠2?

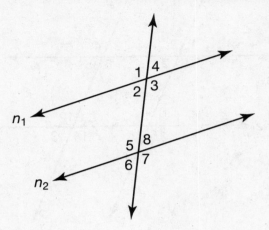

A 35°
B 65°
C 75°
D 115°

6 Lines x and y are parallel. If m∠8 = 66°, what is the measure of ∠6?

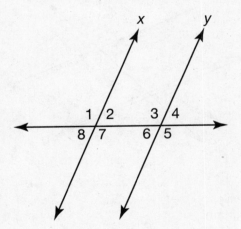

F 24°
G 66°
H 114°
J 124°

7 Lines a and b are parallel. If the measure of ∠1 = 118°, what is the measure of ∠4?

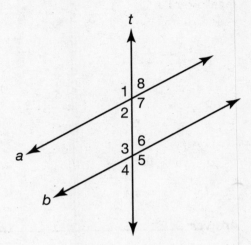

A 59°
B 62°
C 72°
D 118°

8 In parallelogram ABCD, the measure of ∠A is 47°. What is the measure of consecutive ∠B? Write the answer.

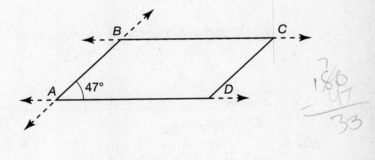

Answer _____

9 In this figure, lines l_1 and l_2 are parallel. Lines m_1 and m_2 are parallel. If $m\angle 11 = 67°$, what is the measure of $\angle 1$?

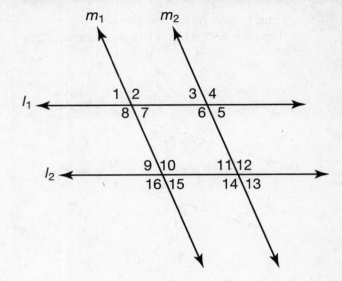

Answer _____

Extended-Response Question

10 In the figure below, lines f and g are parallel, and line t is a transversal.

The measure of $\angle 1 = 66°$.

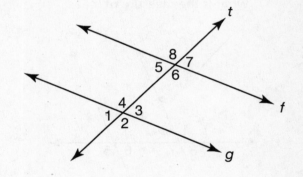

Part A

Which angles in the figure are congruent?

Answer _____

Part B

Are any of the angles in the figure complementary? Explain.

_____

_____

_____

LESSON 26

Strand 3: Geometry

Reflections, Rotations, and Translations on a Coordinate Plane

8.G.7   Describe and identify transformations in the plane using proper function notation (rotations, reflections, translations, and dilations)

8.G.8   Draw the image of a figure under rotations of 90 and 180 degrees

8.G.9   Draw the image of a figure under a reflection over a given line

8.G.10 Draw the image of a figure under a translation

8.G.12 Identify the properties preserved and not preserved under a reflection, rotation, translation, and dilation

A **transformation** is a change in a figure's position and sometimes size. There are four types of transformations you should know. This lesson covers three of those transformations: reflection, rotation, and translation. The figure that results after any of these transformations (sometimes called the image) is congruent to the original figure. That is, the image of a figure after a reflection, rotation, or translation has exactly the same size and shape as the original figure.

REFLECTIONS

A **reflection** is a flip of a figure.

Reflection over the *x*-axis:

If a point is reflected over the *x*-axis, then the image point and the original point lie on the same vertical line and are the same distance from the *x*-axis.

Reflection over the *y*-axis:

If a point is reflected over the *y*-axis, then the image point and the original point lie on the same horizontal line and are the same distance from the *y*-axis.

In the examples in this lesson, the prime symbol (′) is used with each image point to avoid confusion with the original point.

EXAMPLE 1

Reflect △*ABC* over the *x*-axis to form image △*A'B'C'*. Find the coordinates of the vertices of △*A'B'C'*.

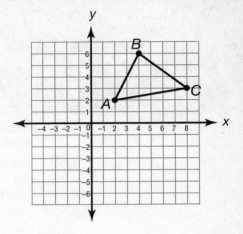

STRATEGY   **Think of what happens to a point when you reflect it over the *x*-axis.**

STEP 1   Find the reflection of each vertex of △*ABC* over the *x*-axis.

Each vertex of the image △*A'B'C'* will be same distance from the *x*-axis but on the opposite side of the *x*-axis.

Vertex *A'* will be on the same vertical line as *A*, but 2 units below the *x*-axis. So the coordinates of A' are (2, −2).

Vertex *B'* will be on the same vertical line as *B*, but 6 units below the *x*-axis. So the coordinates of B' are (4, −6).

Vertex *C'* will be on the same vertical line as *C*, but 3 units below the *x*-axis. So the coordinates of C' are (8, −3).

STEP 2   Graph the vertices *A'*, *B'*, and *C'* and connect them to form a triangle.

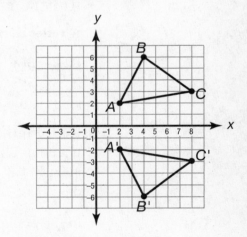

SOLUTION   The coordinates of the image of △*ABC* after a reflection over the *x*−axis are *A'*(2, −2), *B'*(4, −6), and *C'*(8, −3). The graph of △*A'B'C'* is shown in Step 2.

Note in Example 1 that the image of the triangle after the reflection is congruent to the original △*ABC*.

ROTATIONS

A **rotation** is a turn.

The diagram on the left below shows the letter T in the first quadrant and its image after a 90° clockwise turn around a point of rotation. The diagram on the right shows the letter T in the first quadrant and its image after a 180° turn around the point of rotation.

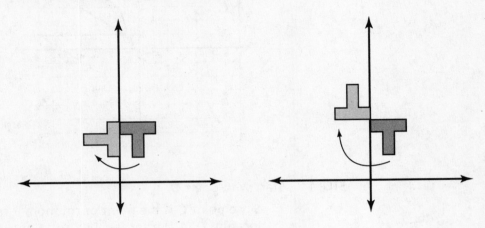

EXAMPLE 2

Rotate △*PQR* 180° clockwise around point *Q* to form image △*P'Q'R'*. What are the coordinates of the vertices of △*P'Q'R'*?

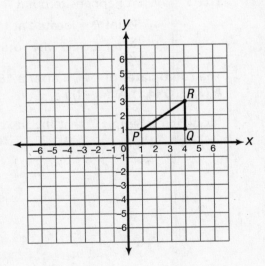

STRATEGY

Draw a new triangle with each vertex rotated 180° clockwise around point *Q*.

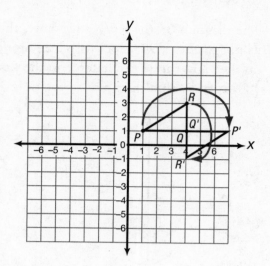

STEP 1   Start with point *Q*.

Since point *Q* is the point of rotation, it remains in the same location *Q'*(4,1) after the 180° rotation.

STEP 2   What happens to point *P* after a 180° clockwise rotation?

Point *P* is located at (1,1).

After a clockwise rotation of 180°, *P* moves to *P'*(7,1).

STEP 3   What happens to point *R* after a 180° clockwise rotation?

Point *R* is located at (4,3).

After a clockwise rotation of 180°, *R* moves to *R'*(4,−1).

SOLUTION

The coordinates of △*PQR* after a 180° clockwise rotation around point *Q* are *P'*(7,1), *Q'*(4,1), *R'*(4,−1).

Notice in Example 2 that the image △*P'Q'R'* is congruent to the original △*PQR*.

TRANSLATIONS

A **translation** is a slide. A translation moves a figure to another position on the graph.

EXAMPLE 3

Find the coordinates of the image of △*HJK* after a translation of 6 units to the left.

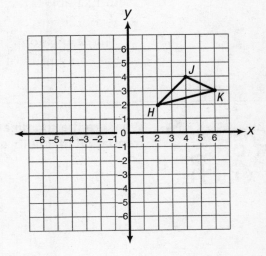

STRATEGY   **Try using a pencil or pen to trace a slide of each vertex of △*HJK*.**

STEP 1   What happens to point *H* when you slide it 6 units to the left?

Point *H* starts at (2,2). After you slide it 6 units to the left, it will end up at *H*′(−4,2).

STEP 2   What happens to point *J* when you slide it 6 units to the left?

Point *J* starts at (4,4). After you slide it 6 units to the left, it will end up at *J*′(−2,4).

STEP 3   What happens to point *K* when you slide it 6 units to the left?

Point *K* starts at (6,3). After you slide it 6 units to the left, it will end up at *K*′(0,3).

This is the graph of the image after the translation.

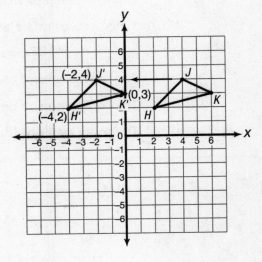

SOLUTION

The coordinate of △HJK after a translation of 6 units to the left are H′(−4,2), J′(−2,4), and K′(0,3).

In Example 3 the x-coordinates of the image vertices are all 6 less than the x-coordinates of the original vertices, and the y-coordinates are the same. This translation can be indicated by the formula $(x − 6, y)$, where (x,y) are the coordinates of a point before the translation.

What are the coordinates of the vertices of the image of △DEF after a translation of 3 units upward?

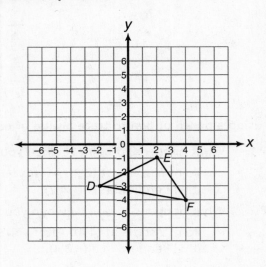

Let's check it out.

When you translate a point up or down, the _____-coordinate of the ordered pair changes.

When you translate a point 3 units up, you _____ 3 to the

_____-coordinate.

The coordinates of the image of vertex D are _____.

The coordinates of the image of vertex E are _____.

The coordinates of the image of vertex F are _____.

Sample Test Questions

1 △*ABC* is reflected over the *x*-axis to form △*A'B'C'*. What are the coordinates of vertex *C'*?

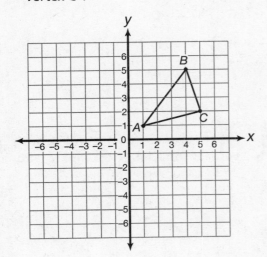

A (−2,5)		**C** (−5,−2)
B (−5,2)		**D** (5,−2)

2 If this triangle was reflected over the *y*-axis to form triangle *H'J'K'*, what would be the coordinates of vertex *K'*?

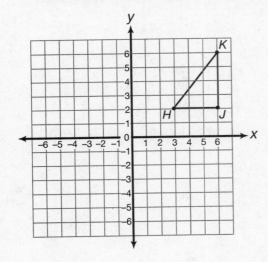

F (6,−6)		**H** (−6,6)
G (6,6)		**J** (−6,−6)

3 What set of coordinates will provide the vertices for a 90° clockwise rotation of △*JKL* around point *K*?

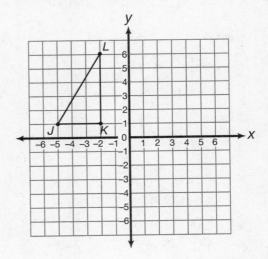

A *J'*(−2,5), *K'*(−2,1), *L'*(4,1)

B *J'*(−2,4), *K'*(−2,1), *L'*(3,1)

C *J'*(−2,5), *K'*(−2,1), *L'*(3,1)

D *J'*(−1,4), *K'*(−2,1), *L'*(3,1)

4 What set of coordinates will provide the vertices for the translation of △*XYZ* two units to the left?

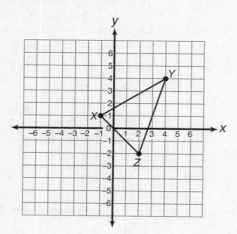

F $X'(1,1)$, $Y'(6,4)$, $Z'(4,-2)$

G $X'(-1,3)$, $Y'(4,6)$, $Z'(2,0)$

H $X'(-3,1)$, $Y'(2,4)$, $Z'(0,-2)$

J $X'(-3,1)$, $Y'(1,4)$, $Z'(-2,0)$

5 What set of coordinates will provide the vertices for the translation of △*HJK* 4 units down?

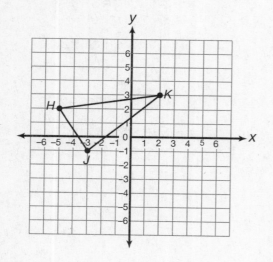

A $H'(-5,-2)$, $J'(-3,-6)$, $K'(4,-1)$

B $H'(-5,2)$, $J'(-3,-5)$, $K'(2,-4)$

C $H'(-5,-4)$, $J'(-3,5)$, $K'(2,-2)$

D $H'(-5,-2)$, $J'(-3,-5)$, $K'(2,-1)$

6 When quadrilateral *PQRS* is reflected over the *y*-axis, how does length of side $P'Q'$ of quadrilateral $P'Q'R'S'$ compare with the length of side *PQ* of quadrilateral *PQRS*?

F $P'Q' > PQ$

G $P'Q' < PQ$

H $P'Q' = PQ$

J $P'Q' = \frac{1}{2}PQ$

7 What set of coordinates will provide the vertices for a 180° clockwise rotation of △*RST* around point *R*?

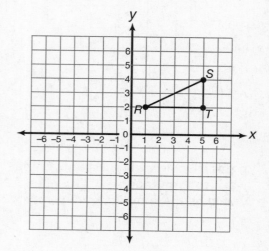

A $R'(1,2)$, $S'(-3,2)$, $T'(-3,4)$

B $R'(1,2)$, $S'(-3,0)$, $T'(-3,2)$

C $R'(2,1)$, $S'(4,5)$, $T'(2,5)$

D $R'(-1,2)$, $S'(-5,2)$, $T'(-5,4)$

8   A translation has this rule: $(x, y + 8)$.
Fill in the answers.

This translation is _____ (how many?)
units _____ (in what direction?).

Answer _____

9   A translation has this rule: $(x - 5, y)$.
Fill in the answers.

This translation is _____ (how many?)
units _____ (in what direction?).

Answer _____

Short-Response Question

10   Stuart is creating a design based on this triangle. As part of his design, he wants to reflect the triangle over the *x*-axis.

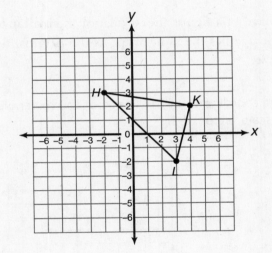

On the grid above, draw the image after the reflection and name the coordinates of the vertices of the image.

H′: _____   *K′*: _____   *L′*: _____

LESSON 27

Strand 3: Geometry

Dilations

8.G.7 Describe and identify transformations in the plane, using proper function notation (rotations, reflections, translations, and dilations)

8.G.11 Draw the image of a figure under a dilation

8.G.12 Identify the properties preserved and not preserved under a reflection, rotation, translation, and dilation

A **dilation** is a transformation that expands or shrinks a figure. The change in the size of the figure depends on the scale factor. If the scale factor is greater than 1, the image is larger than the original figure. If the scale factor is a positive number less than 1, the image is smaller than the original figure.

The image of a figure after a dilation is **similar** to the original figure. That is, the image has the same shape as the original figure but not necessarily the same size.

EXAMPLE 1

Find the coordinates of the image of the rectangle below after a dilation with a scale factor of 2.

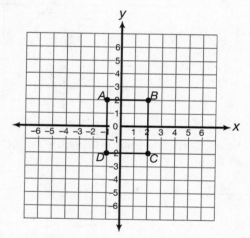

STRATEGY

Multiply the coordinates of the vertices by the scale factor.

$A' = (2 \times -1, 2 \times 2) = (-2,4)$

$B' = (2 \times 2, 2 \times 2) = (4,4)$

$C' = (2 \times 2, 2 \times -2) = (4,-4)$

$D' = (2 \times -1, 2 \times -2) = (-2,-4)$

SOLUTION

The coordinates of the rectangle after a dilation with a scale factor of 2 are $A'(-2,4)$, $B'(4,4)$, $C'(4,-4)$, and $D'(-2,-4)$.

The graph below shows the original rectangle and the rectangle that results after the dilation.

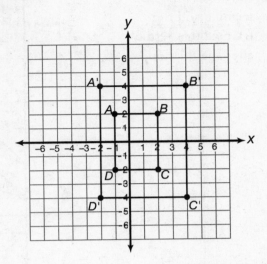

The rectangles are similar, so the corresponding angles are congruent ($\angle A' \cong \angle A$; $\angle B' \cong \angle B$; $\angle C' \cong \angle C$; $\angle D' \cong \angle D$); and the corresponding side lengths are proportional ($\frac{A'B'}{AB} = \frac{B'C'}{BC} = \frac{C'D'}{CD} = \frac{D'A'}{DA}$).

EXAMPLE 2

Find the coordinates of the image of the triangle below after a dilation with a scale factor of $\frac{1}{3}$.

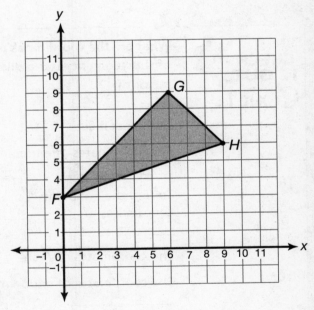

STRATEGY **Multiply the coordinates of the vertices by the scale factor.**

$$F' = (\tfrac{1}{3} \times 0, \tfrac{1}{3} \times 3) = (0,1)$$
$$G' = (\tfrac{1}{3} \times 6, \tfrac{1}{3} \times 9) = (2,3)$$
$$H' = (\tfrac{1}{3} \times 9, \tfrac{1}{3} \times 6) = (3,2)$$

SOLUTION **The coordinates of the triangle after a dilation with a scale factor of $\frac{1}{3}$ are $F'(0,1)$, $G'(2,3)$, and $H'(3,2)$.**

The graph at the right shows the original triangle and the triangle that results after the dilation.

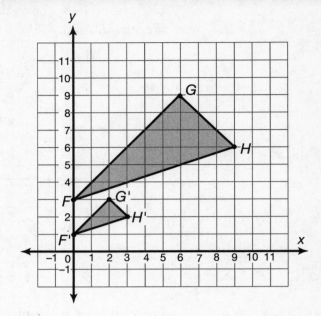

The triangles are similar so the corresponding angles are congruent ($\angle F' \cong \angle F$; $\angle G' \cong \angle G$; $\angle H' \cong \angle H$); and the corresponding side lengths are proportional ($\frac{F'G'}{FG} = \frac{G'H'}{GH} = \frac{H'F'}{HF}$).

CHECK IT OUT *with the* **Coach**™

What are the coordinates of the endpoints of this segment after a dilation with scale factor of $\frac{1}{2}$?

Let's check it out.

The coordinates of endpoint *J* are _____.

To find the endpoint *J'*, multiply the coordinates of _____ by _____.

The coordinates of *J'* are _____.

The coordinates of endpoint *K* are _____.

To find the coordinates of *K'*, multiply the coordinates of _____ by _____.

The coordinates of *K'* are _____.

The coordinates of the endpoints of segment *JK* after a dilation of $\frac{1}{2}$ are _____ and _____.

Sample Test Questions

1 What are the coordinates of △RST after a dilation with a scale factor of 3?

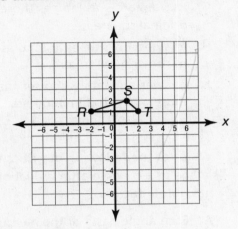

A R′(−6,3), S′(3,6), T′(6,3)

B R′(−$\frac{2}{3}$,1), S′($\frac{1}{3}$,$\frac{2}{3}$), T′(3,1)

C R′(6,3), S′(3,6), T′(6,3)

D R′(−6,3), S′(6,3), T′(3,6)

2 What are the coordinates of △PQR after a dilation with a scale factor of $\frac{2}{3}$?

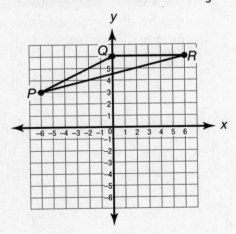

F P′(−2,1), Q′(0,2), R′(2,2)

G P′(−4,2), Q′(0,4), R′(4,4)

H P′(−4,2), Q′(4,0), R′(4,2)

J P′(−12,6), Q′(0,12), R′(12,12)

3 △A′B′C′ is the image of △ABC after a dilation with a scale factor of $\frac{1}{4}$. What are the coordinates of the vertices of △ABC?

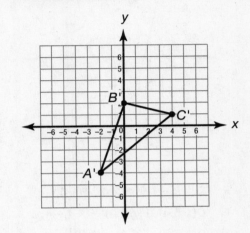

A A(−$\frac{1}{2}$,−1), B(0,$\frac{1}{2}$), C(1,$\frac{1}{4}$)

B A(2,0), B(4,6), C(8,5)

C A(−8,−16), B(0,8), C(16,4)

D A(8,16), B(8,0), C(16,4)

4 △D'E'F' is the image of △DEF after a dilation with a scale factor of 2. What are the coordinates of the vertices of △DEF?

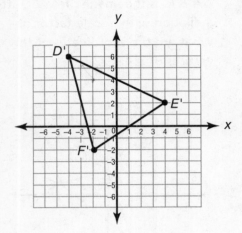

F   D(−8,−12), E(8,4), F(−4,−4)

G   D(−6,4), E(−2,0), F(−4,−4)

H   D(−2,8), E(6,4), F(0,0)

J   D(−2,3), E(2,1), F(−1,−1)

5 Which of the following describes the image of a figure after a dilation that has a scale factor between 0 and 1?

A   It has a different shape from the original figure and is smaller than the original figure.

B   It has the same shape as the original and is larger than the original figure.

C   It has the same shape as the original and is smaller than the original figure.

D   It has the same shape and same size as the original figure.

6 Which of the following describes the image of a square after a dilation that has a scale factor of 6?

F   Its sides are 6 units longer than those of the original square.

G   Its sides are $\frac{1}{6}$ as long as those of the original square.

H   Its sides are 6 times as long as those of the original square.

J   Its sides are 6 units shorter than those of the original square.

7 Which of the following describes the image of a triangle after a dilation that has a scale factor of $\frac{5}{6}$?

A   Each angle has $\frac{5}{6}$ of the measure of its corresponding angle in the original triangle.

B   Each angle has $\frac{6}{5}$ of the measure of its corresponding angle in the original triangle.

C   Each angle has the same measure as its corresponding angle in the original triangle.

D   Each angle is $\frac{1}{6}$ larger than the measure of its corresponding angle in the original triangle.

8 Triangle *PQR* has coordinates *P*(2, 4) *Q*(−2,4), *R*(0,−6). Write the coordinates of the vertices of the image of a triangle after a dilation of 1.5.

Answer ———————————————

9 How does the size of an image compare to the original figure when the original figure undergoes a dilation with a scale factor of 1?

Answer ———————————————

Short-Response Question

10 On the grid below, draw the image of △*FGH* after a dilation with a scale factor of $\frac{1}{2}$.

Show your work.

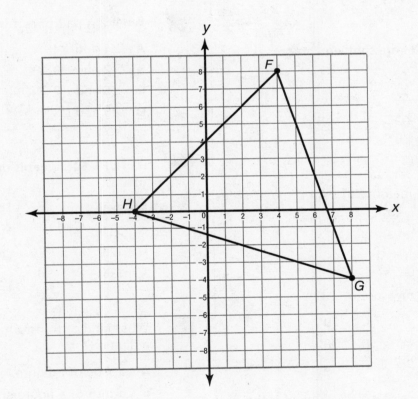

Progress Check for Lessons 24–27

Lines *a*, *b*, *c*, and *d* intersect as shown. Use this figure for Questions 1–4.

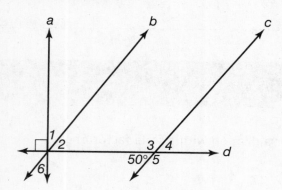

Lines *p* and *q* are parallel and *t* is a transversal. Use this figure for Questions 5 and 6.

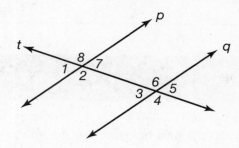

1 Which angles are supplementary?

    A ∠1 and ∠2

    B ∠3 and ∠6

    C ∠4 and ∠5

    D ∠5 and ∠6

2 What is the measure of ∠4?

    F 30°   **H** 50°

    G 40°   **J** 60°

3 What is the measure of ∠3?

    A 40°   **C** 120°

    B 50°   **D** 130°

4 If the measure of ∠1 = 52°, what is the measure of ∠2?

    F 28°   **H** 48°

    G 38°   **J** 128°

5 What is a pair of corresponding angles?

    A ∠1 and ∠4

    B ∠2 and ∠3

    C ∠5 and ∠7

    D ∠5 and ∠8

6 If m∠1 = 54°, what is the measure of ∠6?

    F 36°

    G 54°

    H 126°

    J 136°

7 What kind of transformation is a dilation?

    A a slide of a figure

    B a turn of a figure around a point

    C a stretching or shrinking of a figure

    D a flip of a figure over a line

8 What set of coordinates will provide the vertices for a 180° clockwise rotation of △JKL around point K?

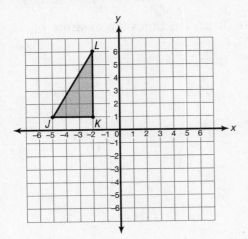

F J′(5,1), K′(2,1), L′(2,6)

G J′(−5,−1), K′(−2,−1), L′(−2,−6)

H J′(−2,4), K′(−2,1), L′(3,1)

J J′(1,1), K′(−2,1), L′(−2,−4)

9 If this triangle was reflected over the x-axis, what would be the coordinates of the vertices of the image?

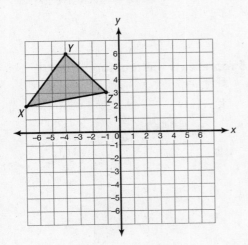

A X′(−7,−2), Y′(−4,−6), Z′(−1,−3)

B X′(7,2), Y′(4,6), Z′(1,3)

C X′(−2,−7), Y′(−6,−4), Z′(−3,−1)

D X′(2,7), Y′(6,4), Z′(3,1)

10 What set of coordinates will provide the vertices for the translation of △HJK 2 units down?

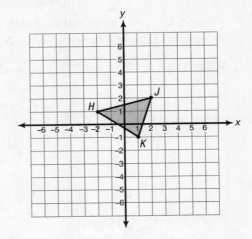

F H′(2,1), J′(−1,2), K′(−2,2)

G H′(−2,−1), J′(1,0), K′(1,−3)

H H′(−2,−1), J′(2,0), K′(1,−3)

J H′(−2,3), J′(2,4), K′(1,1)

11 What set of coordinates will provide the vertices of △ABC after a dilation with a scale factor of 2?

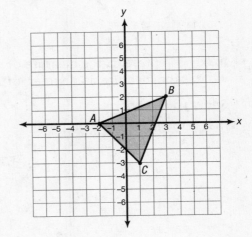

A A′(0,2), B′(5,4), C′(3,−1)

B A′(−4,0), B′(6,4), C′(2,−6)

C A′(4,0), B′(6,4), C′(2,6)

D A′(−4,−2), B′(1,0), C′(−1,−5)

Short-Response Questions

12 ∠*D* and ∠*E* are supplementary angles. The measure of ∠*D* is 5 times the measure of ∠*E*. What is the degree measure of ∠*D*?

Show your work.

Answer _____

13 Line *m* is parallel to line *n*, and line *t* is a transversal.

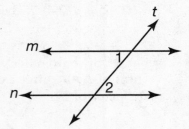

If $3x - 3$ represents the measure of ∠1 and $2x + 15$ represents the measure of ∠2, what is the measure, in degrees, of ∠1?

Show your work.

Answer _____

Extended-Response Question

14

Part A

On the grid below, draw △ *R'S'T'*, the image of △ *RST* after a reflection over the *y*-axis.

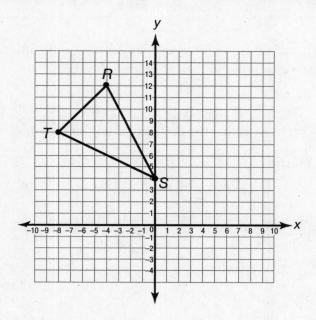

Part B

On the grid above, draw △ *R"S"T"*, the image of △ *R'S'T'* after a dilation with a scale factor of $\frac{1}{2}$.

Part C

How does △ *R"S"T"* compare with △ *RST*?

_____

_____

_____

LESSON 28

Strand 4: Measurement

Converting Measurements

8.M.1 Solve equations/proportions to convert to equivalent measurements within metric and customary measurement systems

This table shows some of the common units in the metric system of measurement and how they are related.

Metric Measurement Equivalencies

Length

1 centimeter (cm) = 10 millimeters (mm)

1 meter (m) = 100 centimeters (cm)

1 kilometer (km) = 1,000 meters (m)

Area

1 square meter (m^2) = 10,000 square centimeters (cm^2)

1 square kilometer (km^2) = 1,000,000 square meters (m^2)

Volume

1 cubic meter = 1,000,000 cubic centimeters (cm^2)

Weight and Mass

1 gram (g) = 1,000 milligrams (mg)

1 kilogram (kg) = 1,000 grams (g)

Capacity

1 liter (L) = 1,000 milliliters (mL)

This table shows some of the common units in the customary system of measurement and how they are related.

Customary Measurement Equivalencies

Length

1 foot (ft) = 12 inches (in.)

1 yard (yd) = 3 feet (ft)

1 mile (mi) = 5,280 feet (ft)

Area

1 square foot (ft^2) = 144 square inches (in.^2)

1 square yard (yd^2) = 9 square feet (ft^2)

1 acre = 4,840 square yards (yd^2)

1 square mile (mi^2) = 640 acres

Volume

1 cubic foot (ft^3) = 1,728 cubic inches (in.^3)

1 cubic yard (yd^3) = 27 cubic feet (ft^3)

Weight and Mass

1 pound (lb) = 16 ounces (oz)

1 ton (T) = 2,000 pounds (lb)

Capacity

1 cup (c) = 8 fluid ounces (fl oz)

1 pint (pt) = 2 cups (c)

1 quart (qt) = 2 pints (pt)

1 gallon (gal) = 4 quarts (qt)

The metric and customary measurement equivalencies above can help you convert between measurements. When you convert between measurements within the same system, there are two rules to remember.

1. When converting from a larger unit to a smaller unit, multiply.

2. When converting from a smaller unit to a larger unit, divide.

EXAMPLE 1

The area of a room is 2,165,000 square centimeters. What is the area of the room in square meters?

STRATEGY   **Use the tables and rules for conversion.**

STEP 1   Find an equivalence in the table.

1 square meter = 10,000 square centimeters

STEP 2   Decide whether to multiply or divide.

The conversion is from a smaller unit to a larger unit, so divide.

2,165,000 ÷ 10,000 = 216.5

SOLUTION   **The area of the room is 216.5 square meters.**

EXAMPLE 2

The volume of a carton is 3.5 cubic feet. What is the volume of the carton in cubic inches?

STRATEGY   **Use the tables and the rules for conversion.**

STEP 1   Find an equivalence in the table.

1 cubic foot = 1,728 cubic inches

STEP 2   Decide whether to multiply or divide.

The conversion is from a larger unit to a smaller unit, so multiply.

$3.5 \times 1,728 = 6,048$

SOLUTION   **The volume of the carton is 6,048 cubic inches.**

You can convert measures by setting up and solving a proportion.

EXAMPLE 3

Darvin has a recipe for making 15 quarts of fruit punch. How many gallons of fruit punch will the recipe make?

STRATEGY   **Use values from the tables to set up a proportion.**

STEP 1   Write a ratio comparing quarts to gallons.

$\dfrac{4 \text{ quarts}}{1 \text{ gallon}}$

STEP 2   Write a ratio comparing 15 quarts to gallons.

Let g represent the number of gallons of fruit punch.

$\dfrac{15 \text{ quarts}}{g \text{ gallons}}$

STEP 3   Set up the proportion and solve.

$\dfrac{4}{1} = \dfrac{15}{g}$ Cross multiply.

$4g = 1 \times 15$

$4g = 15$ Divide both sides by 4 to solve.

$\dfrac{4g}{4} = \dfrac{15}{4}$

$g = \dfrac{15}{4} = 3\dfrac{3}{4}$

SOLUTION   **The recipe will make $3\dfrac{3}{4}$ gallons of fruit punch.**

The following problem deals with converting a measurement expressed in two kinds of units to an equivalent measurement expressed in one kind of unit.

EXAMPLE 4

15 pounds 8 ounces = _____ ounces

STRATEGY

Use the tables and rules for conversion.

STEP 1   Find an equivalence in the table.

1 pound = 16 ounces

STEP 2   Decide whether to multiply or divide.

The conversion is from a larger unit to a smaller unit, so multiply.

$15 \times 16 = 240$

15 pounds 8 ounces = 240 ounces + 8 ounces

SOLUTION

15 pounds 8 ounces = 248 ounces

To convert between Fahrenheit and Celsius temperatures, use these formulas.

From Celsius (C) to Fahrenheit (F):

$$F = \frac{9}{5}C + 32$$

From Fahrenheit (F) to Celsius (C):

$$C = \frac{5}{9}(F - 32)$$

EXAMPLE 5

The average normal temperature in New York City in July is 77°F. What is the average normal temperature in degrees Celsius?

STRATEGY

Use the formula for converting degrees Fahrenheit to degrees Celsius.

STEP 1   Write the formula.

$C = \frac{5}{9}(F - 32)$

STEP 2   Substitute the Fahrenheit temperature in the formula.

$C = \frac{5}{9}(77 - 32)$ Substitute 77 for F.

$= \frac{5}{9}(45)$

$= \frac{5}{9} \times \frac{45}{1}$ Divide the denominator of $\frac{5}{9}$ and the numerator of $\frac{45}{1}$ by 9.

$= 5 \times 5$

$= 25$

SOLUTION

The normal average temperature is 25°C.

CHECK IT OUT *with the* **Coach**™

A truck holds 5,500 pounds of cargo. How many tons of cargo does the truck hold?

Let's check it out.

A ratio comparing pounds to tons is _____.

Let t = the number of tons the truck holds. A ratio comparing the number of pounds the truck holds to the number of tons the truck holds is

_____.

A proportion for solving the problem is _____.

After you cross-multiply the proportion, what equation do you get?

_____

The solution of the equation is _____.

The truck holds _____ tons of cargo.

Sample Test Questions

1 5 gallons 3 quarts = _____ quarts

   A 8 qt

   B 13 qt

   C 15 qt

   D 23 qt

2 The Nelsons purchased 38 square yards of carpeting for their new home. Which proportion can you use to find n, the number of square feet of carpeting they purchased?

   F $\frac{9}{n} = \frac{38}{1}$

   G $\frac{1}{9} = \frac{38}{n}$

   H $\frac{9}{1} = \frac{38}{n}$

   J $\frac{9}{38} = \frac{1}{n}$

3 3.5 m = _____ mm

   A 0.35   **C** 350

   B 35   **D** 3,500

4 175 g = _____ mg

   F 0.175

   G 1,750

   H 17,500

   J 175,000

5 A pitcher holds 1,800 mL of water. How many liters of water does the pitcher hold?

   A 180,000 L

   B 180 L

   C 18 L

   D 1.8 L

6 A piece of property has an area of 0.5 acre. What is the area of the property in square yards?

F 2,420 yd²

G 4,840 yd²

H 9,680 yd²

J 24,200 yd²

7 At 6:00 P.M., the temperature was 15°C. What was the temperature in degrees Fahrenheit?

A 49°F

B 59°F

C 69°F

D 79°F

8 How many 8-ounce glasses will Mitch be able to fill from a 2-gallon jug of orange juice?

Answer _____

9 The volume of the cargo hold in a truck is 11 cubic yards. How many cubic feet is this?

Answer _____

Short-Response Question

10 A rectangular bathroom floor measures 5 ft by 7 ft. Tonya wants to tile the floor with square tiles that measure 1 inch along each side.

How many tiles will Tonya need?

Show your work.

Answer _____ tiles

Practice Test 2

Session 1

1 What is the value of x^{-2} when $x = 5$?

   A $-\dfrac{1}{10}$

   B $-\dfrac{1}{25}$

   C $\dfrac{1}{25}$

   D $\dfrac{1}{10}$

2 The variable m stands for the number of students on the track team last year. This expression represents the number of students on the team this year.

$$2m - 7$$

Which verbal expression matches the expression for the number of students on the team this year?

   F   seven fewer than twice the number of students on last year's team

   G   seven more than twice the number of students on last year's team

   H   the difference between the number of students on last year's team and seven

   J   two more than seven times the number of students on last year's team

3 $3^5 \div 3^2 =$

   A 3^{-3}

   B 3^2

   C 3^3

   D 3^7

4 A computer system has a selling price of $1,150. The sales tax is 8%. What is the total cost of the computer system, including tax?

   F $1,158

   G $1,222

   H $1,230

   J $1,242

5 Solve the equation $3(x + 3) - 4 = 26$ for x.

   A $x = 21$

   B $x = 14$

   C $x = 11$

   D $x = 7$

6 In the triangle below, which is the right angle?

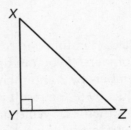

   F $\angle YXZ$

   G $\angle XZY$

   H $\angle XYZ$

   J $\overline{XZ}$

Go On

Test 2: Session 1

7 The average normal temperature in Albany in August is about 20°C. What is this temperature in degrees Fahrenheit?

A   64°F

B   68°F

C   72°F

D   76°F

8 A company's profit for this year is 300% of last year's profit. Which of the following is equivalent to 300%?

F   0.03

G   0.3

H   3

J   30

9 The two legs of a right triangle are 12 cm and 16 cm. What is the length of the hypotenuse?

A   14 cm

B   18 cm

C   20 cm

D   28 cm

10 Walter said, "I'm thinking of a set of whole numbers. If you multiply any of these numbers by 3 and then increase the product by 5, the result is a number that is less than 23." Which inequality can you use to find this set of numbers?

F $3n - 5 < 23$

G $3(n - 5) < 23$

H $3n + 5 < 23$

J $3(5n) < 23$

11 Last year, 78 students participated in the science fair. This year, 102 students participated. Which of the following is the best estimate of the percent increase in participation?

A   20%

B   25%

C   30%

D   35%

12 Lines *JK* and *LM* intersect at point *P*. Ray *PR* is perpendicular to line *JK*.

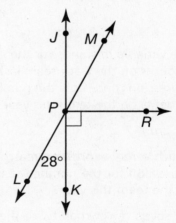

What is the measure of angle *JPL*?

F   142°

G   152°

H   162°

J   172°

13 $\dfrac{75s^7}{-15s^6} =$ _____

A $-5s^{13}$

B $-5s$

C $-1,125s^{13}$

D $-1,125s$

Go On

14 △J′K′L′ is the image of △JKL after a transformation.

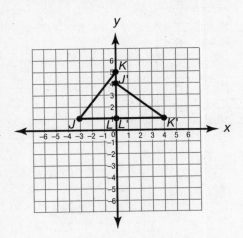

What was the transformation?

F a reflection over the y-axis

G a 90° clockwise rotation around point L

H a 180° clockwise rotation around point L

J a dilation with scale factor $\frac{1}{2}$

15 Keisha invested $29,800 in shares of a company that promises an annual rate of return of 4.8%. Using pencil and paper, she figured that her investment will earn $14,304. Use estimation to choose the correct statement.

A Her calculation is correct.

B Her calculation is about $10,000 too high.

C Her calculation is about $1,000 too high.

D Her calculation is about $100 too low.

16 $(5x − 4)(4x + 3) =$ _____

F $20x^2 − x − 12$

G $20x^2 + x − 12$

H $20x^2 + 31x − 12$

J $20x^2 − 31x − 12$

17 Lines l and m are parallel and line t is a transversal. If $m\angle 1 = (5x − 5)°$ and $m\angle 2 = (2x + 67)°$, what is the measure of $\angle 2$?

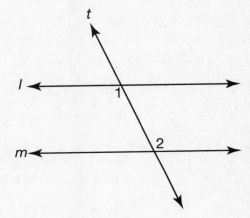

A 95°

B 105°

C 115°

D 125°

18 Simplify the expression.

$$−28 + 11c − 11 + 6c$$

F $17c + 17$

G $17c − 39$

H $5c + 17$

J $5c − 39$

Go On

Test 2: Session 1

19 Which graph matches the table to the right?

x	y
0	10
1	5
2	0
3	−5
4	−10
5	−15

A
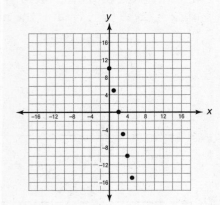

C
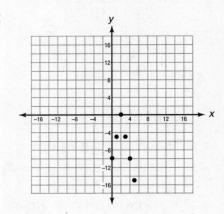

B
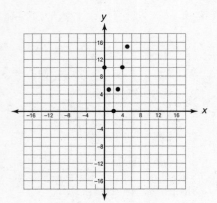

D
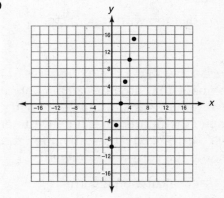

20 Hank drove to visit his cousin who lives 150 miles away. He began driving at 4:00 P.M. This graph shows his progress during the trip.

When did he stop for dinner?

F between 4:00 P.M. and 5:00 P.M.

G between 5:00 P.M. and 7:00 P.M.

H between 7:00 P.M. and 8:00 P.M.

J between 8:00 P.M. and 9:00 P.M.

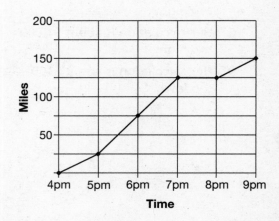

Go On

Test 2: Session 1

21

$$\frac{30a^5 - 15a^3 + 5a^2}{5a^2}$$

A $6a^3 - 3a$

B $6a^3 - 3a + 1$

C $6a^3 - 3a + 5$

D $6a^7 - 3a^5 + a^4$

22 Lines *FG* and *HJ* intersect at point *X*.

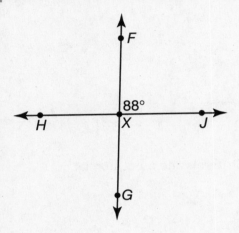

Which statement is true?

F m∠*HXG* = 88°, m∠*FXH* = 92°, m∠*JXG* = 92°

G m∠*HXG* = 88°, m∠*FXH* = 92°, m∠*JXG* = 88°

H m∠*HXG* = 88°, m∠*FXH* = 88°, m∠*JXG* = 92°

J m∠*HXG* = 92°, m∠*FXH* = 88°, m∠*JXG* = 88°

23 What is $n^2 + n - 6$ in factored form?

A $(n + 1)(n - 6)$

B $(n - 1)(n + 6)$

C $(n + 2)(n - 3)$

D $(n + 3)(n - 2)$

24 Which set of the dimensions below will form a right triangle?

F 9 cm, 16 cm, 20 cm

G 9 cm, 20 cm, 25 cm

H 9 cm, 14 cm, 17 cm

J 9 cm, 12 cm, 15 cm

25 The distance between two cities on a map is $2\frac{1}{4}$ inches. The scale of the map is $\frac{1}{4}$ in. = 4 miles. What is the actual distance between the cities?

A 12 miles

B 20 miles

C 28 miles

D 36 miles

26 It costs $12.00 to buy 150 cases of Brand A boxes. It costs $16.50 to buy 175 cases of Brand B boxes. Which brand has the better value and by approximately how much?

F Brand A: 1 cent

G Brand A: 2 cents

H Brand B: 1 cent

J Brand B: 2 cents

27 The area of a piece of land owned by the Patel family is represented by the polynomial $15x^2 + 13x + 2$. The area of the land next to theirs is represented by the polynomial $9x^2 - 6x + 1$. If they buy the land next to theirs, which polynomial will represent the total area of their land?

A $24x^4 + 7x^2 + 3$

B $24x^2 + 7x + 3$

C $24x^2 + 19x + 3$

D $24x^2 - 19x + 3$

STOP

Test 2: Session 1

Session 2

28 A DVD player that regularly sells for $160 goes on sale for $120. What is the percent discount?

Show your work.

Answer _____ %

29 Study the terms in this trinomial.

$$32n^4 + 40n^3 - 8n^2$$

Part A

Write the polynomial as the product of the GCF of all its terms and a polynomial.

Answer _____

Part B

Explain how you determined your answer to Part A.

_____

_____

30 Look at the function table.

Part A

Write the equation that shows how to determine the value of *y* for any value of *x*?

Answer _____

Part B

Use the equation to find the corresponding *y*-values for *x* = 6, 7, and 8.

Answer _____

x	y
0	5
1	9
2	13
3	17
4	21
5	25

Go On

31 Melissa bought a rectangular lot that measures 180 feet by 240 feet.

What is the area of Melissa's lot in square yards?

Show your work.

Answer _____ square yards

32 △ABC is graphed on the coordinate grid below.

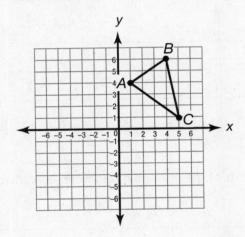

Part A

Graph △A′B′C′, the image of △ABC after a translation of 8 units down.

Part B

How do the size and shape of △A′B′C′ compare with the size and shape of △ABC?

_____

Part C

On the coordinate grid above, graph △A″B″C″, the image of △A′B′C′ after a reflection over the *y*-axis.

Part D

How did you determine the coordinates of the vertices of △A″B″C″?

_____

_____

_____

Go On

33 Look at the trinomial below.

$x^2 + 2x - 15$

Part A

Factor the trinomial as the product of two binomials.

Answer _____

Part B

Use what you know about binomials and trinomials to explain how you found your answer to Part A.

_____

_____

_____

_____

Part C

Suppose the middle term of the trinomial had been $-2x$ instead of $2x$. How would the factored form change?

_____

_____

_____

_____

STOP

Session 3

34 $\dfrac{4^5}{4^3} = 4^n$

What is the value of *n* in the equation above?

Show your work.

Answer _____

35   This is a linear equation.

$y = -\dfrac{1}{2}x + 3$

Part A

Complete this table of values for the equation.

x	y
−4	
−2	
0	
2	
4	

Part B

Use the values from the table in Part A
to graph the equation at the right.

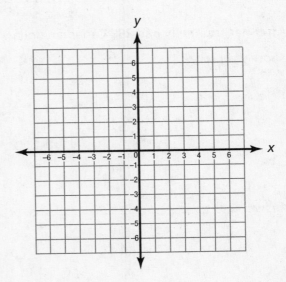

Go On

Test 2: Session 3

36   Last year, Megumi's salary was $41,235. This year, she got a raise of $1,987. Estimate the percent increase in Megumi's salary.

Show your work.

Answer _____

37   During her trip to Canada, Kelly learned that 1 Canadian dollar was equivalent to the value of 0.8 U.S. dollars.

Part A

Kelly began her trip with $3,000 U.S. dollars. How many Canadian dollars did Kelly have?

Show your work.

Answer _____ Canadian dollars

Part B

After her trip, Kelly had 396 Canadian dollars left. What was the value in U.S. dollars?

Show your work.

Answer $ _____

Go On

38 Jonah used the digits 2, 3, and 4 to form this expression.

$(2^3)^4$

What is the value of Jonah's expression?

Show your work.

Answer _____

39 Tova bought 3 bottles of juice, each holding 750 mL.

Part A

Write a proportion to find x, the number of liters of juice Tova bought.

Answer _____

Part B

Solve your proportion to find the number of liters of juice Tova bought.

Show your work.

Answer _____

Go On

40 This rectangle is the model for the product of two binomials. In the model, each small square represents 1, each rectangle represents x, and the large square represents x^2.

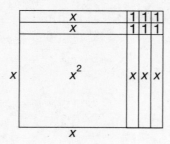

The area of the rectangle is the product of the length and the width. The length of the rectangle above is $x + 3$ and the width is $x + 2$. The rectangle is made up of 1 large square plus 5 rectangles plus 6 small squares, which is $x^2 + 5x + 6$, the product you would get if you multiplied the binomials $x + 3$ and $x + 2$.

What two binomials would give the product shown in the model below?

Show your work.

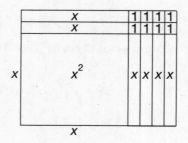

Answer _____

Go On

194   Test 2: Session 3   Duplicating any part of this book is forbidden by law.

41 Sarah is shopping for a new air conditioner. The model she wants to buy costs $615. This week, a store advertises that the model will be on sale at a 40% discount. Sarah uses her calculator to find the amount of discount and gets $246.00.

Part A

How can you use estimation to check the reasonableness of Sarah's calculation?

_____

_____

Part B

Without doing the calculation, tell whether or not Sarah's calculator result is reasonable. Explain your answer.

_____

_____

_____

42 Lines *p* and *q* intersect to form angles 1, 2, 3, and 4. The measure of ∠1 is 72°.

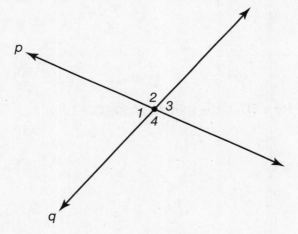

Part A

What is the measure of ∠2?

Answer _____

Part B

Explain why your answer to Part A is correct.

_____

_____

Go On

Part C

What is the measure of ∠3?

Answer _____

Part D

Explain why your answer to Part C is correct.

_____

_____

43   It costs $35 for a spindle of 105 blank CD's. It costs $170 for a spindle of 500 blank CD's.

Part A

What is the unit price for a CD in the spindle of 105 CD's?

Show your work.

Answer $_____

Part B

What is the unit price for a CD in the spindle of 500 CD's?

Show your work.

Answer $_____

Part C

Which spindle of CD's is the better buy?

Answer _____

Go On

Test 2: Session 3

44   △*DEF* is graphed below.

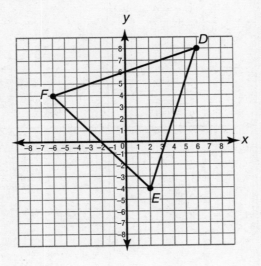

Part A

What are the coordinates of the vertices of △*D'E'F'*, the image of △*DEF*, after a dilation with a scale factor of $\frac{1}{2}$?

Answer _____

Part B

On the coordinate grid above, graph △*D'E'F'*.

Part C

How do the size and shape of △*D'E'F'* compare with the size and shape of △*DEF*?

_____

_____

_____

_____

Go On

45 Figure I and Figure II are graphed below.

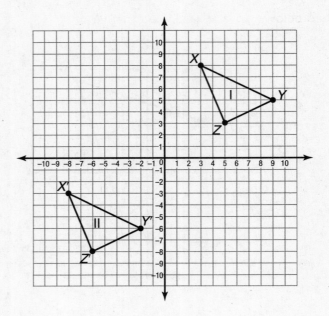

Part A

Explain how Figure 1 was transformed to Figure 2.

_____

_____

_____

Part B

Are Figure 1 and Figure 2 congruent? Explain.

_____

_____

_____

STOP

FORMULAS		CONVERSIONS
Pythagorean Theorem		Temperature Conversion $F = \frac{9}{5}C + 32$ $C = \frac{5}{9}(F - 32)$
Simple Interest	$I = prt$	
Distance Formula	$d = rt$	Measurement Conversions 1 mile = 5,280 feet 1 yard = 3 feet
Slope-Intercept Formula	$y = mx + b$ m = slope b = y-intercept	

LESSON 29

Strand 2: Algebra

Solving Multi-Step Linear Inequalities

8.A.13 Solve multi-step inequalities and graph the solution set on a number line

8.A.14 Solve linear inequalities by combining like terms, using the distributive property, or moving variables to one side of the inequality (include multiplication or division of inequalities by a negative number)

8.G.19 Graph the solution of an inequality on a number line

You solve an inequality in much the same way that you solve an equation. The goal is the same—to isolate the variable—but with inequalities, you must keep this rule in mind:

When multiplying or dividing both sides of an inequality by a negative number, change the direction of the inequality.

For example, if the inequality uses $<$ and you multiply or divide both sides by a negative number, you must change $<$ to $>$.

A good way to show the solution of an inequality is to graph it on a number line.

EXAMPLE 1

Solve and graph the solution of this inequality:

$$4x + 11 \geq 19$$

STRATEGY **Use the method for solving an equation.**

STEP 1 Subtract to isolate the variable.

$$4x + 11 \geq 19$$
$$4x + 11 - 11 \geq 19 - 11 \qquad \text{Subtract 11 from both sides.}$$
$$4x + 0 \geq 8$$
$$4x \geq 8$$

STEP 2 Complete the isolation of the variable by dividing.

$$4x \geq 8 \qquad \text{Divide both sides by 4.}$$
$$\frac{4x}{4} \geq \frac{8}{4} \qquad \text{Dividing both sides by } \textit{positive } 4 \text{ does not change the direction of the inequality symbol.}$$

$$x \geq 2$$

The solution is 2 and all numbers greater than 2.

STEP 3   Graph the solution.

Draw a number line.

Since 2 is part of the solution, a solid dot goes on 2.

Draw a ray from 2 to the right to represent all numbers greater than 2.

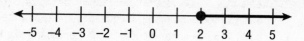

SOLUTION

The solution of $4x + 11 \geq 3$ is $x \geq 2$. The graph of the solution is shown in Step 3.

EXAMPLE 2

Solve and graph the solution of this inequality:

$$-2(x - 4) - 3x < 23$$

STRATEGY

Use the method for solving an equation.

STEP 1   Simplify the left side of the inequality.

$-2(x - 4) - 3x < 23$	Use the Distributive Property.
$-2x + 8 - 3x < 23$	Use the Commutative Property.
$-2x - 3x + 8 < 23$	Combine like terms.
$-5x + 8 < 23$	

STEP 2   Solve the inequality.

$-5x + 8 < 23$	
$-5x + 8 - 8 < 23 - 8$	Subtract 8 from both sides.
$-5x + 0 < 15$	
$-5x < 15$	
$\dfrac{-5x}{-5} > \dfrac{15}{-5}$	Divide both sides by -5. Change the direction of the inequality.
$x > -3$	

The solution is all numbers greater than -3.

STEP 3   Graph the solution.

Draw a number line.

Since -3 is not part of the solution, an open circle goes on -3.

Draw a ray from -3 to the right to represent all numbers greater than -3.

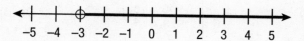

SOLUTION

The solution of $-2(x - 4) - 3x < 23$ is $x > -3$. The graph of the solution is shown in Step 3.

EXAMPLE 3

Solve and graph the solution of this inequality:

$$9x + 4 \leq 3x - 14$$

STRATEGY   **Use the method for solving an equation.**

STEP 1   Get the variable on one side of the inequality symbol.

$$9x + 4 \leq 3x - 14$$
$$9x - 3x + 4 \leq 3x - 3x - 14 \qquad \text{Subtract } 3x \text{ from both sides.}$$
$$6x + 4 \leq 0 - 14$$
$$6x + 4 \leq -14$$

STEP 2   Solve.

$$6x + 4 \leq -14$$
$$6x + 4 - 4 \leq -14 - 4 \qquad \text{Subtract 4 from both sides.}$$
$$6x + 0 \leq -18$$
$$6x \leq -18$$
$$\frac{6x}{6} \leq -\frac{18}{6} \qquad \text{Divide both sides by 6.}$$
$$x \leq -3$$

The solution is −3 and all numbers less than −3.

STEP 3   Graph the solution.

Draw a number line.

Since −3 is part of the solution, a solid dot goes on −3.

Draw a ray from −3 to the left to represent all numbers less than −3.

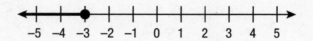

SOLUTION   **The solution of 9x + 4 ≤ 3x − 14 is x ≤ −3. The graph of the solution is shown in Step 3.**

What is the graph of the solution of $5x + 3 < 2x + 15$?

Let's check it out.

Get the variables on one side of the inequality by subtracting $2x$ from both sides. The resulting inequality is _____.

Begin to isolate the variable by subtracting 3 from both sides. The resulting inequality is _____.

Complete isolating the variable by dividing both sides by the same number. The resulting inequality is _____

Describe the solution of the inequality in words. _____

Graph the solution on the number line below.

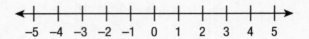

Sample Test Questions

1 Solve for x: $2x + 3 > 15$

   A $x > 6$

   B $x < 6$

   C $x > 9$

   D $x < 9$

2 Solve for x: $-8x + 1 < 25$

   F $x < 3$

   G $x > 3$

   H $x > -3$

   J $x < -3$

3 Solve for x: $4(x + 5) \leq 16$

   A $x \geq -1$

   B $x \leq -1$

   C $x \geq 1$

   D $x \leq 1$

4 Solve for n: $3n + 7 - n > 21$

   F $n > 14$

   G $n < 14$

   H $n < 7$

   J $n > 7$

5 Which of the following is the graph of the solution of this inequality?

$$-6n + 4 \geq 28$$

A

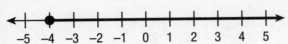

B

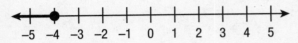

C

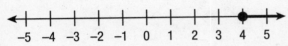

D

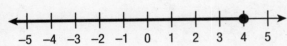

6 Which of the following is the graph of the solution of this inequality?

$$2x + 3x - 5 < 15$$

F

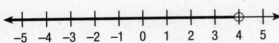

G

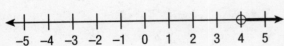

H

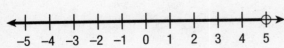

J

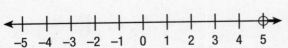

7 Which of the following is the graph of the solution of this inequality?

$$9x + 4 \leq -6x + 49$$

A

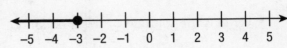

B

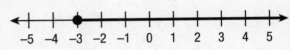

C

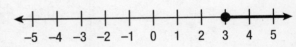

D

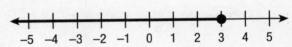

8 Write the solution for y.

$$11y - 2 \leq 3y + 14$$

Answer _____

9 Write the solution for Q.

$$5Q + 8 > -4Q - 19$$

Answer _____

Short-Response Question

10

Part A

What is the solution of this inequality?

$$-2(n + 1) - 3 < 1$$

Show your work.

Answer _____

Part B

Graph the solution on the number line below.

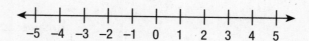

LESSON 30

Strand 2: Algebra

Relations and Functions

8.A.17 Define and use correct terminology when referring to function (domain and range)

8.A.18 Determine if a relation is a function

An **ordered pair** names the location of a point on a coordinate grid. The x-coordinate (the first coordinate) tells you how far to the right or left of 0 the point is, and the y-coordinate tells you how far up or down from 0 the point is.

A **relation** is a set of ordered pairs, for example, $\{(-4,3), (4,9), (5,12)\}$.

The **domain** of a relation is the set of x-values of the relation. The **range** of a relation is the set of y-values of the relation. For the relation shown above, the domain is $\{-4, 4, 5\}$ and the range is $\{3, 9, 12\}$.

A **function** is a relation in which each element of the domain corresponds to one and only one element of the range. In terms of ordered pairs, a function is a relation in which no two ordered pairs have the same x-coordinate. The relation above has no two x-coordinates that are the same, so that relation is a function.

EXAMPLE 1

Is the following relation a function? Why or why not?

$\{(1,5), (2,10), (3,15), (4,20)\}$

STRATEGY

Use the definition of function.

STEP 1   List the x-coordinates.

1, 2, 3, 4

STEP 2   Do any of the x-coordinates repeat?

Each x-coordinate appears only once. Another way of stating this is that each x-coordinate (domain value) is paired with exactly one y-coordinate (range value).

SOLUTION

The relation is a function because each member of the domain is paired with exactly one member of the range.

Relations and functions are sets of ordered pairs, so they can be graphed on a coordinate plane. Here is a graph of the relation {(4,2), (4,5), (6,8), (10,8)}.

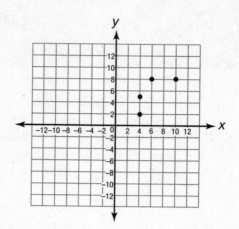

If the graph of a relation has more than one y-coordinate for an x-coordinate, then the relation is not a function. There is an easy way to check if there is more than one y-coordinate for each x-coordinate. If you can draw a vertical line through more than one point on the graph, then the relation is not a function.

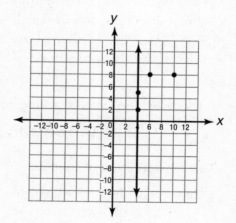

A vertical line can be drawn through two points, so the relation {(4,2), (4,5), (6,8), (10,8)} is not a function.

EXAMPLE 2

Does the graph show a function? If so, why?

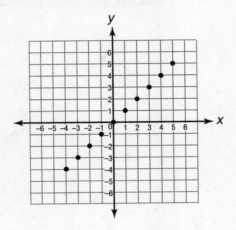

STRATEGY

Use the vertical line test.

It is not possible to draw a vertical line through more than one point.

SOLUTION

The graph shows a function because it is impossible to draw a vertical line through more than one point.

The relation in Example 2 has a finite (countable) number of points. The vertical line test can also be used for relations that consist of an infinite number of points.

EXAMPLE 3

The following graph shows a relation with an infinite number of points. Does the graph represent a function? Why or why not?

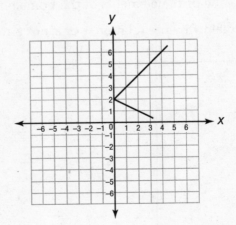

STRATEGY

Use the vertical line test.

You can draw a vertical line through two points at many locations. One example would be the points at (2,1) and (2,4).

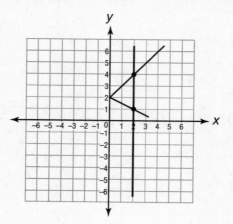

SOLUTION

The graph is not a function because it is possible to draw a vertical line that intersects the graph in more than one point.

Is this relation a function?

   {(−2,4), (−1,1), (0,0), (1,1), (2,4)}

Let's check it out.

The domain of the relation is _____.

The range of the relation is _____.

Do any of the elements of the domain repeat? _____

Explain why the relation is or is not a function. _____

_____

Sample Test Questions

1 What is the range of this relation?

{(1,2), (3,4), (5,6), (7,8), (7,10)}

A {1, 3, 5, 7, 8}

B {5, 6, 7, 8, 10}

C {2, 4, 6, 7, 8}

D {2, 4, 6, 8, 10}

2 Which relation is a function?

F {(1,3), (2,2), (3,3), (3,4)}

G {(10,15), (20,40), (20,45), (30,50)}

H {(12,28), (14,28), (16,30), (18,32)}

J {(22,11), (24,12), (26,12), (26,13)}

3 Which relation is a function?

A {(−1,1), (2,8), (−1,−1), (−2,−8)}

B {(1,2), (2,8), (3,18), (2,32)}

C {(−3,9), (−2,4), (2,4), (3,9)}

D {(1,5), (2,10), (−2,10), (1,15)}

4 Which relation is not a function?

F $\{(\frac{1}{2},\frac{1}{3}), (\frac{1}{4},\frac{1}{5}), (\frac{1}{6},\frac{1}{7}), (\frac{1}{8},\frac{1}{9})\}$

G $\{(\frac{1}{2},\frac{2}{2}), (\frac{1}{3},\frac{3}{2}), (\frac{2}{3},\frac{2}{3}), (\frac{3}{3},\frac{4}{3})\}$

H $\{(\frac{1}{2},\frac{1}{5}), (\frac{3}{2},\frac{1}{6}), (\frac{4}{2},\frac{1}{7}), (\frac{5}{2},\frac{1}{8})\}$

J $\{(\frac{1}{2},\frac{1}{4}), (\frac{1}{4},\frac{1}{8}), (\frac{4}{8},\frac{1}{16}), (\frac{4}{16},\frac{1}{32})\}$

5 Which graph below does not show a function?

A

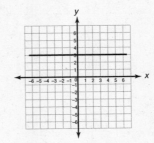

B

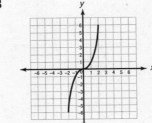

C

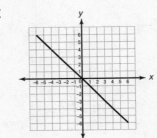

D

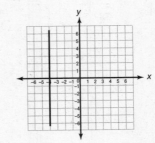

6 Which graph shows a function?

F

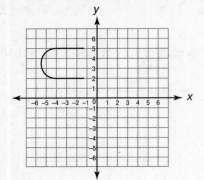

H

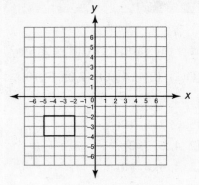

G

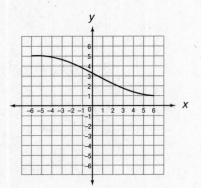

J

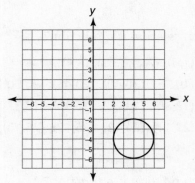

7 Which graph shows a function?

A

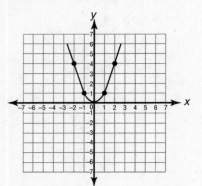

C

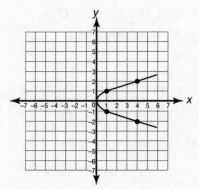

B

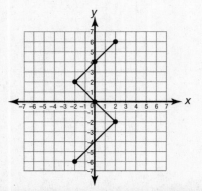

D

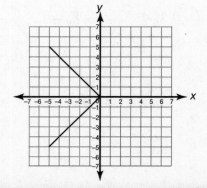

8 Write the domain of this relation.

{(5,25), (6,36), (−5,25), (−6,36)}

Answer _____

9 Write the range of this relation.

{(2,20), (2,−40), (−2,10), (−2,−30)}

Answer _____

Extended-Response Question

10

Part A

Determine if the relation below is a function.

{(−3,8), (−2,3), (−1,0), (0,−1), (1,0), (2,3), (3,8)}

Answer _____

Part B

How could you explain your answer to Part A using a graph?

_____

_____

_____

_____

LESSON
31

Strand 2: Algebra

Representing Relations

8.A.19 Interpret multiple representations using equation, table of values and graph

You can express the same relation in different ways. The next three examples show some of the different ways to represent and solve problems about the relation of the number of miles in a cab ride to the total cost of the ride.

EXAMPLE 1

The ABC Cab Company charges a flat fee of $4.00 plus $2.00 for each mile or part of a mile. What is the cost of a 2-mile trip? A 5-mile trip? A $7\frac{1}{2}$-mile trip?

STRATEGY

Use the verbal description to set up arithmetic problems.

STEP 1 Find the cost of a 2-mile trip.

flat fee + cost of 2 miles

$4.00 + 2.00 \cdot 2 = 4.00 + 4.00 = 8.00$

STEP 2 Find the cost of a 5-mile trip.

flat fee + cost of 5 miles

$4.00 + 2.00 \cdot 5 = 4.00 + 10.00 = 14.00$

STEP 3 Find the cost of a $7\frac{1}{2}$-mile trip.

Since the company charges $2.00 for each whole mile or part of a mile, a $7\frac{1}{2}$-mile trip costs the same as an 8-mile trip.

flat fee + cost of $7\frac{1}{2}$ miles

$4.00 + 2.00 \cdot 8 = 4.00 + 16.00 = 20.00$

SOLUTION

The cost of a 2-mile trip is $8.00; the cost of a 5-mile trip is $14.00; and the cost of a $7\frac{1}{2}$-mile trip is $20.00.

You can express the relation of the number of miles to total cost as an equation.

EXAMPLE 2

Write an equation for finding the cost of a taxi ride in the previous example based on the number of miles of the trip. Then use the formula to find the cost of a 20-mile trip.

STRATEGY   **Use key words in the description to write the equation. Then substitute 20 in the equation.**

STEP 1   Choose variables.

Let m = the number of miles in a ride.

Let C = the cost of a ride.

STEP 2   Write an expression for the cost from the information in the problem.

flat fee + cost per mile · number of miles

4.00 + 2.00   · number of miles

4.00 + 2.00   · m

So the expression is $4 + 2m$, *or* $2m + 4$.

STEP 3   Set the expression equal to the cost.

$C = 2m + 4$

STEP 4   Use the equation to find the cost of a 20-mile ride.

$C = 2m + 4$

$= 2 \cdot 20 + 4$

$= 40 + 4$

$= 44$

SOLUTION   **An equation for finding the cost of a cab ride is $C = 2m + 4$, and cost of a 20-mile ride is \$44.**

Now that you have an equation for finding the cost of a cab ride, you can graph the relation.

EXAMPLE 3

Graph the relation of the number of miles of a cab ride to the cost of the cab ride in the previous example.

STRATEGY

Use the formula to generate a set of ordered pairs.

STEP 1 Make a table to find ordered pairs of the form (m,C).

m	$C = 2m + 4$	C	(m,C)
1	$C = 2(1) + 4 = 2 + 4 = 6$	6	$(1,6)$
2	$C = 2(2) + 4 = 4 + 4 = 8$	8	$(2,8)$
3	$C = 2(3) + 4 = 6 + 4 = 10$	10	$(3,10)$
4	$C = 2(4) + 4 = 8 + 4 = 12$	12	$(4,12)$

STEP 2 Plot the points from the table.

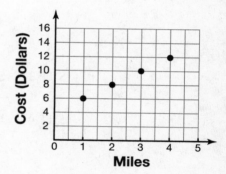

STEP 3 Complete the graph.

Think of the situation.

You pay the cost of 1 mile ($6) for any distance you ride up to and including 1 mile. You show this by graphing a horizontal line segment for $C = 6$ from $m = 0$ to $m = 1$. The left end of the segment has an open circle because you pay $4 to go 0 miles. The right end of the segment has a dot because you pay $6 for any distance you ride up to and including 1 mile.

You pay the cost of 2 miles ($8) for any distance you ride that is greater than 1 mile and less than or equal to 2 miles. Show this by graphing a horizontal line segment for $C = 8$ from $m = 1$ to $m = 2$. The left end of the segment has an open circle because you pay $6 to go 1 mile. The right end of the segment has a dot because you pay $8 for any distance you ride up to and including 2 miles.

Continuing the pattern results in this graph.

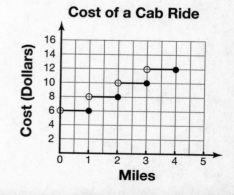

Cost of a Cab Ride

SOLUTION

The graph of the relation is shown in Step 3.

CHECK IT OUT with the Coach

Suppose a rival cab company charges a flat fee of $2 and $2 per mile. How can you represent this situation as an equation, a table of ordered pairs, and a graph?

Let's check it out.

Let C represent the total cost of a ride and m represent the number of miles in the ride.

Use the variables to represent the situation as an equation:

cost of a ride = cost of 1 mile · number of miles + flat fee _____

Substitute values in the equation to represent the situation as a table of values.

m	C
1	
2	
3	
4	

Represent the situation with a graph.

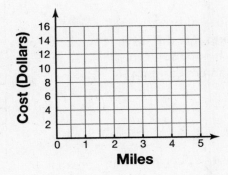

Sample Test Questions

Use this situation for Questions 1–4.

Manny repairs computers in people's homes. He charges $20 for a house call and $20 for each hour or part of an hour he works.

1 Which arithmetic expression can you use to find the total amount Manny will make for a job that requires a house call and lasts 4 hours 20 minutes?

A $20 + 4 \cdot 20$

B $20 + 4\frac{1}{3} \cdot 20$

C $20 + 5 \cdot 20$

D $(20 + 20) \cdot 5$

2 If h represents the number of hours Manny works and T represents the total amount he makes, which equation can be used to represent Manny's earnings for a repair job?

F $T = 20h - 20$

G $T = 20h + 20$

H $T = 20(h - 20)$

J $T = 20(h + 20)$

3 If h represents the number of hours Manny works and T represents the total amount he makes, which table represents Manny's earnings for a repair job?

A
h	T
1	40
2	60
3	80
4	100
5	120

B
h	T
1	20
2	40
3	60
4	80
5	100

C
h	T
0	40
1	60
2	80
3	100
4	120

D
h	T
0	20
2	80
4	140
6	200
8	260

4 Which graph best represents Manny's earnings for a repair job?

F

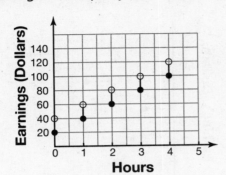

G

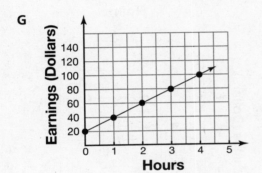

H

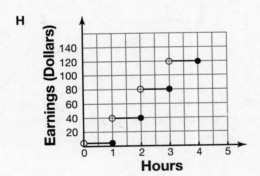

J

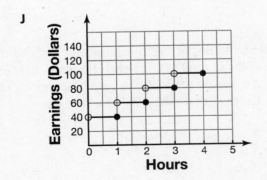

Use this situation for Questions 5–8.

Carmela works as a technology consultant to companies that make computer games. For a recent job, she was paid $200 in traveling expenses, and $50 per hour or part of an hour.

5 Which arithmetic expression can you use to find the total amount Carmela will be paid for the job if she worked $7\frac{3}{4}$ hours?

A $7\frac{3}{4}(200 + 50)$

B $200 + 7\frac{3}{4} \cdot 50$

C $50 + 8 \cdot 200$

D $200 + 8 \cdot 50$

6 If h represents the number of hours Carmela works and T represents the total amount she makes when her travel expenses are $200, which table represents Carmela's earnings for a consulting job?

F

h	T
1	150
2	200
3	250
4	300
5	350

H

h	T
1	250
2	300
3	350
4	400
5	450

G

h	T
1	200
2	250
3	300
4	350
5	400

J

h	T
1	200
2	300
3	400
4	500
5	600

7 Which graph best represents Carmela's earnings for a consulting job when she gets $200 in travel expenses?

A

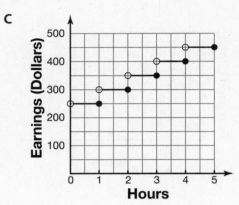

C

B

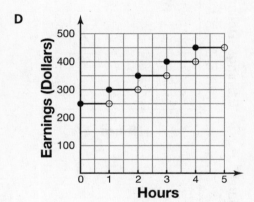

D

8 If h represents the number of hours Carmela works and T represents the total amount she makes, write an equation that can be used to represent Carmela's earnings when she receives $200 in travel expenses?

Answer _____

9 Louise gets paid different amounts for different tasks she does at her company. She gets paid $12 for each hour she spends answering the phone and she gets $15 for each hour she spends filling orders. Let h_1 stand for the number of hours she answers the phone and h_2 stand for the number of hours she fills orders. Write an equation for the total amount P she receives.

Answer _____

Extended-Response Question

10 This table represents the number of hours Chandler worked and the amount of money he earned.

Hours (h)	Earnings (E)
1	32
2	44
3	56
4	68
5	80

Part A

Write an equation to represent Chandler's earnings.

Equation _____

Part B

Explain how you determined the equation.

_____

_____

_____

Part C

How can you check your equation?

_____

_____

_____

LESSON

32

Strand 3: Geometry

Geometric Constructions

8.G.0 Construct the following using a straight edge and compass:
Segment congruent to a segment
Angle congruent to an angle
Perpendicular bisector
Angle bisector

The basic tools for making geometric constructions are the compass and straight edge. The following are four constructions you should know.

HOW TO CONSTRUCT A
SEGMENT CONGRUENT TO A GIVEN SEGMENT

Congruent segments are segments that have the same length.

EXAMPLE 1

Construct a segment congruent to $\overline{RS}$.

R   S

STRATEGY

Follow these steps.

STEP 1 Place the point of the compass on endpoint R of $\overline{RS}$. Adjust the opening of the compass so that the pencil point is at endpoint S of $\overline{RS}$.

STEP 2 Draw $\overrightarrow{PT}$.

STEP 3 Using the compass setting from Step 1, place the point of the compass on endpoint P of $\overrightarrow{PT}$ and draw an arc through $\overrightarrow{PT}$. Use Q to label the point of intersection of the ray and the arc.

P   Q   T

SOLUTION

Segment PQ is congruent to given segment RS.

HOW TO CONSTRUCT A
PERPENDICULAR BISECTOR OF A SEGMENT

A **perpendicular bisector** of a segment is a line, a ray, or another segment that is perpendicular to the given segment at its midpoint. The perpendicular bisector forms right angles with the given segment and divides the given segment into two congruent segments.

EXAMPLE 2

Construct the perpendicular bisector of $\overline{MN}$.

STRATEGY

Follow these steps.

STEP 1 Place the point of the compass on endpoint M of $\overline{MN}$. Draw an arc that intersects the segment. Make sure that the compass setting is greater than half the length of $\overline{MN}$.

STEP 2 Keep the same compass setting. Then place the point of the compass on endpoint N of $\overline{MN}$ and draw a second arc that intersects the first arc at two points. Call these points J and K.

STEP 3 Draw $\overleftrightarrow{JK}$ that intersects $\overline{MN}$ at point Z. $\overleftrightarrow{JK}$ is perpendicular to $\overline{MN}$ and divides $\overline{MN}$ into two congruent segments.

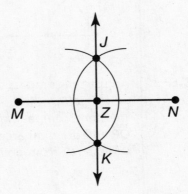

SOLUTION

$\overleftrightarrow{JK} \perp \overline{MN}$, and $\overline{MZ} \cong \overline{ZN}$.

HOW TO CONSTRUCT AN
ANGLE CONGRUENT TO A GIVEN ANGLE

Congruent angles are angles that have the same measure.

EXAMPLE 3

Construct an angle congruent to ∠A.

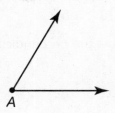

STRATEGY

Follow these steps.

STEP 1   Set the compass point on vertex *A* and draw an arc that intersects the sides of ∠*A*. Label the points of intersection *B* and *C*. Draw $\overrightarrow{OP}$. Keeping the same compass setting, place the point of the compass on endpoint *O* and draw an arc that intersects $\overrightarrow{OP}$. Label the point of intersection *Q*.

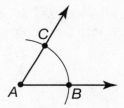 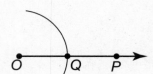

STEP 2   Adjust the compass setting so that the point is on point *B* and the pencil point is on point *C*. Draw an arc through point *C*. Keeping the same compass setting, place the compass point on point *Q* of $\overrightarrow{OP}$ and draw an arc that intersects the arc you drew in Step 1. Draw a ray from point *O* through the intersection of the arcs.

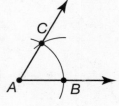 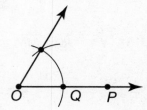

SOLUTION   ∠**O** ≅ ∠**A**

HOW TO CONSTRUCT AN ANGLE BISECTOR

An **angle bisector** divides an angle into two congruent angles.

EXAMPLE 4

Construct the angle bisector of ∠ABC.

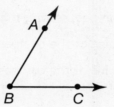

STRATEGY

Follow these steps.

STEP 1   Place the compass point at vertex *B*. Draw an arc that intersects the sides of angle *B*. Label the points of intersection *X* and *Y*.

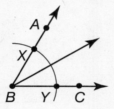

STEP 2   Place the point of the compass on point *X* and draw an arc in the interior of the angle. Keeping the same compass setting, place the compass point on point *Y* and draw an arc that intersects the interior arc at point *P*.

STEP 3   Draw ray *BP*, the bisector of ∠ABC.

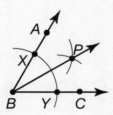

SOLUTION

$\overrightarrow{BP}$ **is the angle bisector of ∠ABC, and ∠ABP ≅ ∠PBC.**

Angles that are congruent have the same measure. A shorthand for writing "the measure of ∠ABP equals the measure of ∠PBC" is m∠ABP = m∠PBC.

CHECK IT OUT with the Coach™

How can you construct a perpendicular bisector of $\overline{AB}$?

A •————————• B

Let's check it out.

Choose a compass setting that is greater than _____.

With the point of the compass on _____, draw an arc.

With the point of the compass on _____, draw an arc equal to the first one you drew.

Draw a line *l* through the points where _____.

Label point *M*, the intersection of line *l* and $\overline{AB}$.

Show the construction:

A •————————————• B

_____ is perpendicular to _____.

_____ is congruent to _____.

Sample Test Questions

1 What does this drawing illustrate?

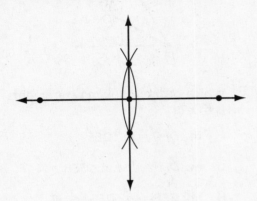

A how to construct the bisector of an angle

B how to construct the perpendicular bisector of a segment

C how to construct a segment congruent to a given segment

D how to construct an angle congruent to a given angle

2 What does this drawing illustrate?

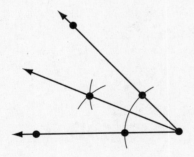

F how to construct the bisector of an angle

G how to construct the perpendicular bisector of a segment

H how to construct a segment congruent to a given segment

J how to construct an angle congruent to a given angle

3 What does this drawing illustrate?

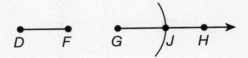

A how to construct the bisector of an angle

B how to construct the perpendicular bisector of a segment

C how to construct a segment congruent to a given segment

D how to construct an angle congruent to a given angle

4 What does this drawing illustrate?

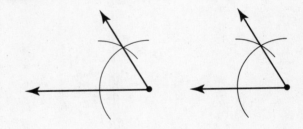

F how to construct the bisector of an angle

G how to construct the perpendicular bisector of a segment

H how to construct a segment congruent to a given segment

J how to construct an angle congruent to a given angle

5 In the figure below, line p is the perpendicular bisector of $\overline{JK}$.

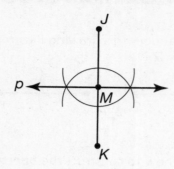

Which of the following statements is true?

A $JK = \frac{1}{2}JM$

B $JK = 2MK$

C $JM = 2MK$

D $2JM = \frac{1}{2}MK$

6 In the figure below, $\overrightarrow{EG}$ is the bisector of $\angle DEF$.

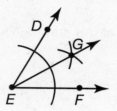

Which of the following statements is true?

F $m\angle DEG = m\angle DEF$

G $m\angle DEF = \frac{1}{2} \times m\angle GEF$

H $m\angle GEF = m\angle DEG$

J $m\angle GEF = 2 \times m\angle DEG$

Short-Response Questions

7

Part A

On ray *XY* below, construct an angle that is congruent to ∠*Q*.

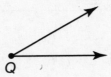

Q

Part B

Explain how you constructed the congruent angle in Part A.

_____

_____

_____

8

Part A

Construct $\overleftrightarrow{DE}$, the perpendicular bisector of $\overline{RS}$.

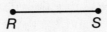

R   S

Part B

Explain how you constructed the perpendicular bisector.

_____

_____

_____

LESSON

33

Strand 3: Geometry

Slope

8.G.13 Determine the slope of a line from a graph and explain the meaning of slope as a constant rate of change.

The **slope** of a line is the ratio of the vertical change to the corresponding horizontal change. You can determine the vertical change and horizontal change from any two points on the line.

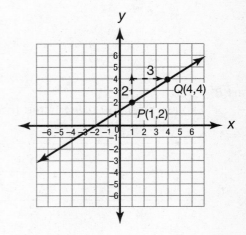

Follow these steps to find the slope of the line shown above:

1. Locate any two points on the line, such as P and Q.

2. Find the vertical change (the rise) from P to Q.

   Count the number of units of vertical change from P to Q.

   The rise is 2 units.

   (You can also determine the rise by finding the difference of the y-coordinates of P and Q: $4 - 2 = 2$.)

3. Find the horizontal change (the run) from P to Q.

   Count the number of units of horizontal change from P to Q.

   The run is 3 units.

   (You can also determine the run by finding the difference of the x-coordinates of P and Q: $4 - 1 = 3$.)

4. Form a ratio of the rise to the run.
   $$\frac{\text{rise}}{\text{run}} = \frac{2}{3}$$

5. Check to see if the line rises or falls from left to right. Since this line rises from left to right, the slope is positive. (If the line had fallen from left to right, then the slope would be negative.)
   So the slope of the line above is $\frac{2}{3}$.

EXAMPLE 1

What is the slope of the line that passes through points *A* and *B*?

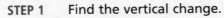

STRATEGY

Since the points have already been chosen for you, follow the steps, starting with step 2.

STEP 1   Find the vertical change.

Counting units, there is a vertical change of 6 units.

STEP 2   Find the horizontal change.

Counting units, there is horizontal change of 3 units.

STEP 3   Form a ratio of rise to run.

$$\frac{\text{rise}}{\text{run}} = \frac{6}{3} = \frac{2}{1}$$

STEP 4   Check to see if the line rises or falls from left to right.

The line falls, so the slope is negative.

SOLUTION

The slope of the line is $\frac{-2}{1}$, or -2.

If you know the coordinates of two points on a line, such as (x_1, y_1) and (x_2, y_2), you can find the slope *m* of the line using this formula:

$$m = \frac{y_1 - y_2}{x_1 - x_2}$$

For Example 1 above, let the coordinates of $A(-2,5)$ be (x_1, y_1) and the coordinates of $B(1,-1)$ be (x_2, y_2).

$$m = \frac{y_1 - y_2}{x_1 - x_2} = \frac{5 - (-1)}{-2 - 1}$$

$$= \frac{5 + 1}{-2 - 1}$$

$$= \frac{6}{-3}$$

$$= -2$$

Remember: You can choose any two points on a line to find the slope because the ratio of vertical change to horizontal change remains constant along a straight line.

A **rate** is a fixed ratio between quantities of different units. For example:

$$\frac{60 \text{ miles}}{1 \text{ hour}} \qquad \frac{\$50}{2 \text{ hours}} \qquad \frac{\$2.50}{1 \text{ gallon}}$$

You can determine rates from graphs by finding the slope.

EXAMPLE 2

An eighth-grade art class decided to sell hand-painted T-shirts to raise money for a field trip. This graph compares the number of T-shirts painted to the number of hours it took to do the painting.

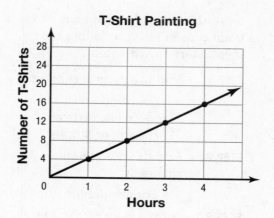

At what rate did the students paint?

STRATEGY **Find the slope of the line to find the rate.**

STEP 1 Write the slope formula.

$$m = \frac{y_1 - y_2}{x_1 - x_2}$$

STEP 2 Choose coordinates of two points from the graph.

The coordinates of two points on the graph are (2,8) and (3,12).

(Remember, you could choose any other two points. The result will be the same.)

STEP 3 Substitute the coordinates in the slope formula.

Let $(3,12) = (x_1, y_1)$ and $(2,8) = (x_2, y_2)$.

$$\text{slope } (m) = \frac{\text{rise}}{\text{run}} = \frac{y_1 - y_2}{x_1 - x_2}$$

$$= \frac{12 - 8}{3 - 2}$$

$$= \frac{4}{1} = 4$$

STEP 4 Translate the slope into a rate.

$$\text{slope} = \frac{4}{1} = \frac{\text{number of T-shirts}}{\text{number of hours}}$$

SOLUTION **The students painted 4 T-shirts per hour.**

What is the slope of this line?

Let's check it out.

The coordinates of point *A* are

_____.

The coordinates of point *B* are

_____.

The vertical change from *A* to *B* is

_____ units.

The horizontal change from *A* to *B* is

_____ units.

The ratio of rise to run is _____.

The line rises from left to right so the sign of the slope is _____.

The slope of the line is _____.

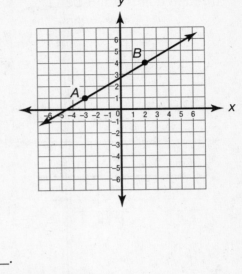

Sample Test Questions

1 What is the slope of the line that passes through points *R* and *S*?

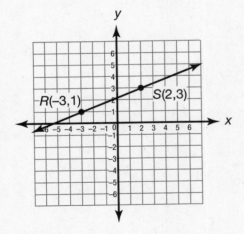

A $-\frac{5}{2}$ **C** $\frac{2}{5}$

B $-\frac{2}{5}$ **D** $\frac{5}{2}$

2 What is the slope of the line that passes through points *J* and *K*?

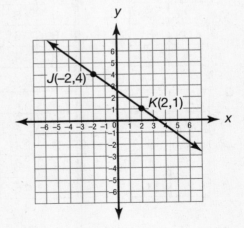

F $-\frac{4}{3}$ **H** $\frac{3}{4}$

G $-\frac{3}{4}$ **J** $\frac{4}{3}$

3 What is the slope of the line that passes through points *P* and *Q*?

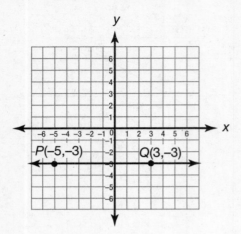

A   −3

B   0

C   1

D   2

4 Which table shows a constant rate of change in the corresponding *x*-values and *y*-values?

F

x	y
1	4
2	5
3	8
4	9

H

x	y
0	9
3	8
6	6
9	4

G

x	y
0	2
1	5
2	8
3	11

J

x	y
0	2
2	4
4	8
6	16

5 Ernesto rode on a train that traveled at a constant rate. The graph compares the number of hours traveled to the number of miles traveled.

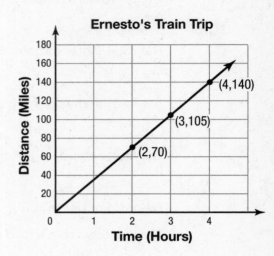

What was the rate of speed of the train?

A   35 miles per hour

B   70 miles per hour

C   105 miles per hour

D   140 miles per hour

6 This graph shows the number of pies produced at a bakery as a function of time.

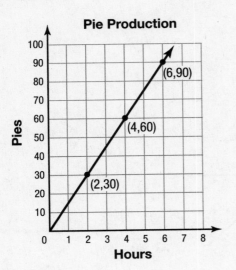

Pie Production

What is the rate of pie production?

F 10 pies per hour

G 15 pies per hour

H 30 pies per hour

D 60 pies per hour

7 This graph shows the growth of a plant in Martha's window box.

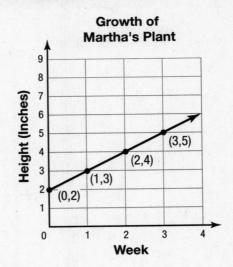

Growth of Martha's Plant

What is the rate of growth of Martha's plant?

A $\frac{1}{2}$ inch per week

B 1 inch per week

C 2 inches per week

D 5 inches per week

8 What is the slope of a line going through points $(-2, -3)$ and $(-4, -5)$?

Answer _____

9 A line with slope of 2 passes through the points (2,5) and (4,?). Find the missing number of the second ordered pair.

Answer _____

Short-Response Question

10   What is the slope of this line?

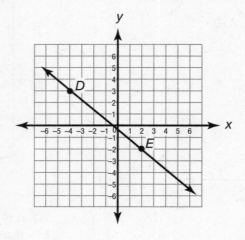

Show your work.

Answer _____

LESSON 34

Strand 3: Geometry

Determining the y-Intercept of a Line

8.G.14 Determine the y-intercept from a graph and be able to explain the y-intercept

8.G.15 Graph a line using a table of values

You can graph a linear equation by setting up a table of values. The values in the table provide ordered pairs. You plot the ordered pairs and draw a line through them to complete the graph.

EXAMPLE 1

Graph the equation $y = -2x + 2$.

STRATEGY

Make a table of ordered pairs to determine some of the points on the line.

STEP 1 Make a table of x-values and y-values. Use the table to find three or four ordered pairs that can be graphed as points on a coordinate grid.

x	y = –2x + 2	y	(x,y)
–2	y = –2(–2) + 2 = 4 + 2 = 6	6	(–2,6)
0	y = –2(0) + 2 = 0 + 2 = 2	2	(0,2)
2	y = –2(–2) + 2 = –4 + 2 = –2	–2	(2,–2)
3	y = –2(3) + 2 = –6 + 2 = –4	–4	(3,–4)

STEP 2 Graph the ordered pairs and draw a straight line through the points.

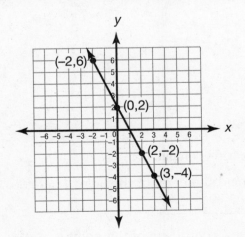

SOLUTION

The graph in Step 2 is the graph of $y = -2x + 2$.

The **y-intercept** of a line is the y-coordinate of the point where the line crosses the y-axis. In the graph above, the line crosses the y-axis at the point with coordinates (0,2). The y-coordinate of this point is 2, so the y-intercept of the line is 2.

EXAMPLE 2

What is the y-intercept of this line?

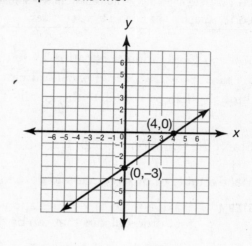

STRATEGY   **Find the point where the line crosses the y-axis.**

The line crosses the y-axis at the point with coordinates (0,−3).
The y-coordinate of this point is the y-intercept of the line.
So, the y-intercept is −3.

SOLUTION   **The y-intercept of the line is −3.**

CHECK
IT OUT
with the
Coach™

What is the y-intercept of this line?

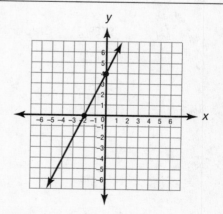

Let's check it out.

The coordinates of the point where the line crosses the y-axis are

_____.

The y-coordinate of this point is _____.

So, the y-intercept of this line is _____.

Sample Test Questions

1 Which graph matches this table of values?

x	−4	−2	0	4
y	0	1	2	4

A

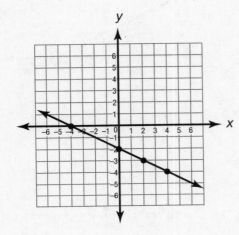

C

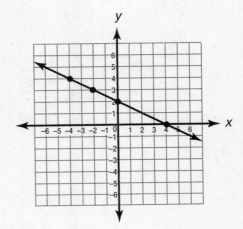

B

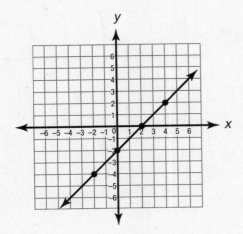

D

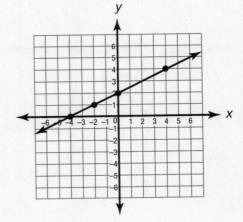

2 Which graph matches this table of values?

x	−4	0	2	4
y	4	2	1	0

F

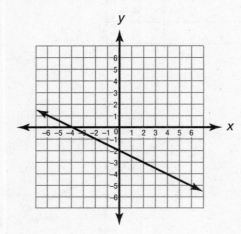

H

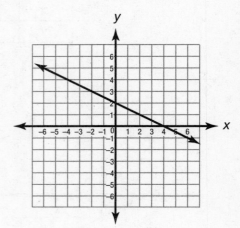

G

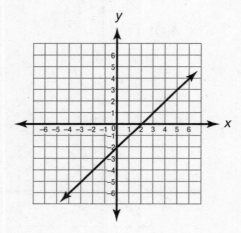

J

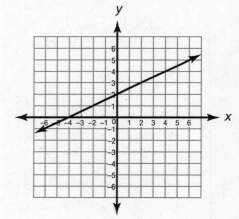

3 Which is the graph of this equation? [Hint: Make a table of values.]

$y = -3x + 6$

A

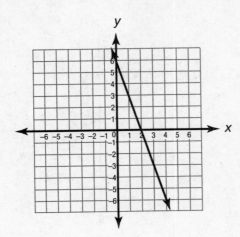

C

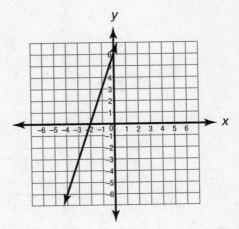

B

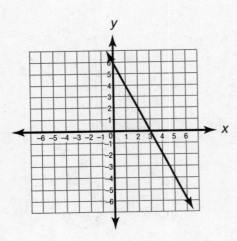

D

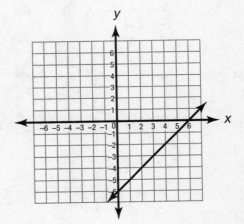

4 Which is the graph of this equation? [Hint: Make a table of values.]

$$y = \frac{1}{2}x + 1$$

F

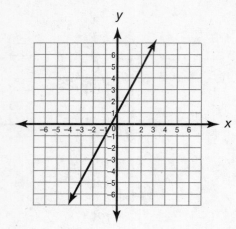

H

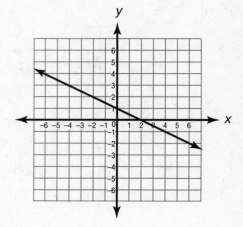

G

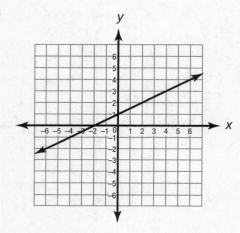

J

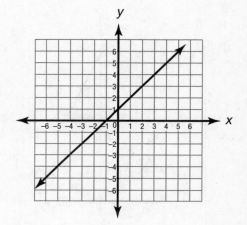

5 What is the *y*-intercept of this graph?

A −4

B −2

C 0

D 2

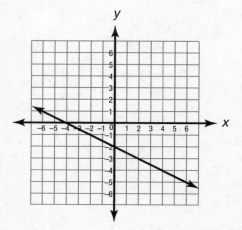

6 What is the *y*-intercept of this graph?

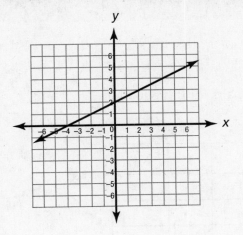

F −4

G −2

H 0

J 2

7 What would be the *y*-intercept of the graph of the line formed by this table of values?

x	y
−2	6
−1	4
0	2
1	0
2	−2

A −2

B −1

C 1

D 2

8 What is the *y*-intercept of this graph?

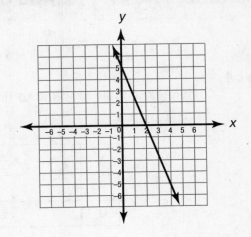

Answer _____

9 A table of values is made from the equation $y = 3x - 1$. Fill in the missing values.

x	y
−2	
−1	
2	
	0
	−1

Extended-Response Question

10

Part A

Complete the table of values to find the ordered pairs for this equation.

$$y = -\frac{1}{2}x + 2$$

x	$y = -\frac{1}{2}x + 2$	y	(x,y)
–4			
0			
4			
8			

Part B

Graph the equation on the grid below

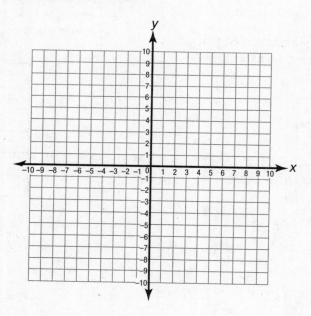

Part C

What is the *y*-intercept of the line you graphed in Part B?

Answer _____

LESSON 35

Strand 3: Geometry

Slope-Intercept Form of a Line

8.G.16 Determine the equation of a line given the slope and the y-intercept

8.G.17 Graph a line from an equation in slope-intercept form ($y = mx + b$)

The linear equations you graphed in Lesson 34 were in this form:

$$y = mx + b$$

In this form, called the **slope–intercept form**, m stands for the slope of the line, and b stands for the y-intercept of the line.

EXAMPLE 1

What is the slope and y-intercept of the graph of the linear equation $y = -x + 3$?

STRATEGY **Compare the equation to the slope-intercept form of a linear equation.**

Since $-x = -1x$, you can rewrite the equation as $y = -1x + 3$.

Compare the equation to the slope-intercept form.

$$y = -1x + 3$$
$$\downarrow \qquad \downarrow$$
$$y = mx + b$$

So, $m = -1$ and $b = 3$.

SOLUTION **The slope of the line is -1 (which you can think of as $\frac{-1}{1}$), and the y-intercept is 3.**

If an equation is in slope–intercept form, you can quickly graph the equation without making a table of values.

EXAMPLE 2

Graph the linear equation $y = \frac{3}{4}x - 2$.

STRATEGY **Use the slope and y-intercept from the equation.**

STEP 1 Identify the slope and y-intercept.

The equation $y = \frac{3}{4}x - 2$ is in the form $y = mx + b$.

So, slope $= m = \frac{3}{4}$, and y-intercept $= b = -2$.

STEP 2   Graph the equation.

Graph the ordered pair for the *y*-intercept: $(0, -2)$. Since $m = \frac{3}{4} = \frac{\text{rise}}{\text{run}}$, start at $(0, -2)$ and count 3 units up and 4 units across to find another point on the line.

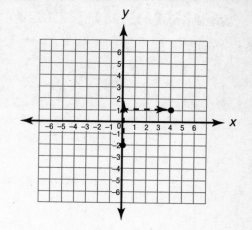

STEP 3   Draw a line through the two points.

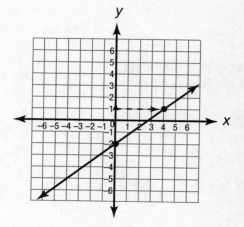

SOLUTION   The line in Step 3 is the graph of $y = \frac{3}{4}x - 2$.

CHECK IT OUT *with the* **Coach**™

What is the graph of the equation $y = 2x - 6$?

Let's check it out.

The *y*-intercept is _____,

so the graph crosses the *y*-axis

at the point with coordinates

_____.

The slope of the line is _____.

Count _____ unit(s) up and

_____ unit(s) across from

the point where the graph crosses the

y-axis. The coordinates of the second point are _____.

Draw a line through the two points.

Sample Test Questions

1 What is the slope of the line whose equation is $y = 2x + 7$?

   A $\frac{1}{2}$

   B 2

   C 3.5

   D 7

2 What is the slope of the line whose equation is $y = -4x + 8$?

   F -4

   G $-\frac{1}{4}$

   H 4

   J 8

3 What is the y-intercept of the line whose equation is $y = 3x - 4$?

   A -4

   B -3

   C 3

   D 4

4 What are the coordinates of the point where the graph of the equation $y = -2x + 3$ crosses the y-axis?

   F (3,0)

   G (0,−2)

   H (0,3)

   J (−2,3)

5 What are the coordinates of the point where the graph of the equation $y = 3x - 3$ crosses the y-axis?

   A (3,0)

   B (0,3)

   C (−3,0)

   D (0,−3)

6 A line has a slope of $-\frac{3}{2}$ and a y-intercept of 6. What is the equation of the line?

   F $y = -\frac{3}{2}x + 6$

   G $y = -\frac{3}{2}x - 6$

   H $y = 6x - \frac{3}{2}$

   J $y = -6x - \frac{3}{2}$

7 A line has a slope of 5 and a y-intercept of -1. What is the equation of the line?

   A $y = -1x + 5$

   B $y = 5x - 1$

   C $y = 5x + 1$

   D $y = \frac{1}{5}x - 1$

8 What are the slope and y-intercept of the line with equation $y = 3x$?

Answer _____

9 Write the equation of a line with slope $\frac{3}{4}$ and y-intercept -10.

Answer _____

Short-Response Question

10 On the coordinate grid below, use the slope and y-intercept to graph the equation $y = \frac{5}{2}x - 4$.

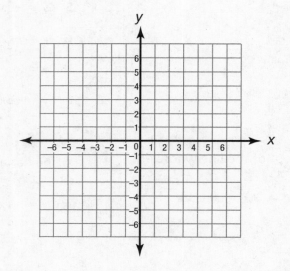

LESSON 36

Strand 3: Geometry

Linear and Nonlinear Graphs

8.G.20 Distinguish between linear and nonlinear equations $ax^2 + bx + c$; $a = 1$ (only graphically)

An equation is **linear** if its graph is a straight line. An equation is **nonlinear** if its graph is not a straight line.

EXAMPLE 1

Determine whether or not the equation $y = -x + 4$ is linear.

STRATEGY

Graph some points and see if they form a straight line.

STEP 1 Plot some of the points in the graph.

The equation is in slope-intercept form, $y = mx + b$.

Therefore, the slope is -1, and the y-intercept is 4.

Plot the point where the line crosses the y-axis: (0,4).

Since the slope is negative, count 1 unit down and 1 unit to the right to find another point: (1,3).

Starting at (1,3), count another 1 unit down and 1 unit to the right to find another point: (2,2).

Starting at (2,2), count another 1 unit down and 1 unit to the right to find another point: (3,1).

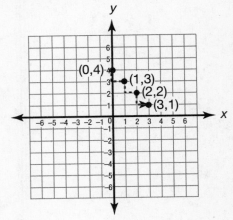

STEP 2 Try to draw a straight line through the points.

It is possible to draw a straight line through all the points.

SOLUTION

The equation $y = -x + 4$ is linear because its graph is a straight line.

EXAMPLE 2

Determine whether or not the equation $y = x^2 - 4$ is linear.

STRATEGY

Graph some points and see if they form a straight line.

STEP 1   Graph some of the points.

This equation is not in slope-intercept form, so make a table of values.

x	$y = x^2 - 4$	y	(x,y)
–3	$y = (-3)^2 - 4 = 9 - 4 = 5$	5	(–3,5)
–2	$y = (-2)^2 - 4 = 4 - 4 = 0$	0	(–2,0)
0	$y = (0)^2 - 4 = 0 - 4 = -4$	–4	(0,–4)
2	$y = (2)^2 - 4 = 4 - 4 = 0$	0	(2,0)
3	$y = (3)^2 - 4 = 9 - 4 = 5$	5	(3,5)

STEP 2   Try to draw a straight line through the points.

It is impossible to draw a straight line through all the points. It is possible, however, to connect the points with a curve.

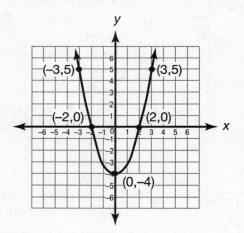

SOLUTION

The equation $y = x^2 - 4$ is nonlinear because it is impossible to draw a straight line that contains all its points.

This is a graph you saw in Lesson 31:

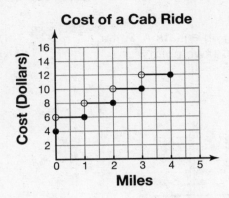

Is this graph linear?

Let's check it out.

There is a horizontal line segment connecting points at (0,6) and

_____.

There is a horizontal line segment connecting points at (1,8) and

_____.

Is there one straight line that connects all the points in all the segments?

_____

Therefore, this graph is _____.

Sample Test Questions

1 Hakeem is graphing an equation. So far, he has graphed these two points.

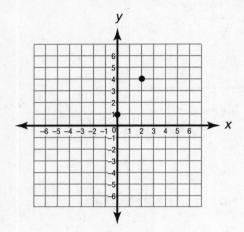

What conclusion can you draw about the equation Hakeem is graphing?

A It is linear.

B It is nonlinear.

C It is impossible to tell whether it is linear or nonlinear until he graphs more points.

D It is neither linear nor nonlinear.

2 Doreen is graphing an equation. So far, she has graphed these points.

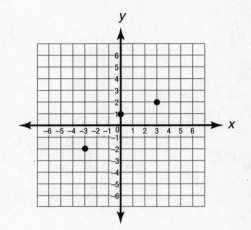

What conclusion can you draw about the equation Doreen is graphing?

F It is linear.

G It is nonlinear.

H It is impossible to tell whether it is linear or nonlinear until she graphs more points.

J It is neither linear nor nonlinear.

3 How can you describe the equation that has this graph?

A It is linear.

B It is nonlinear.

C It is both linear and nonlinear.

D It is neither linear nor nonlinear.

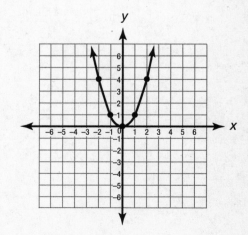

4 How can you describe the equation that has this graph?

F It is linear.

G It is nonlinear.

H It is both linear and nonlinear.

J It is neither linear nor nonlinear.

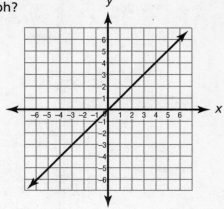

5 Which is the graph of a nonlinear equation?

A

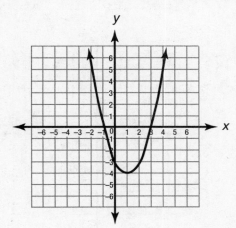

C

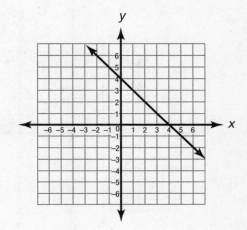

B

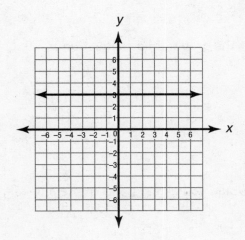

D

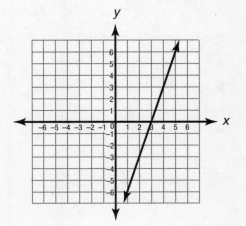

6   Which is the graph of a linear equation?

F

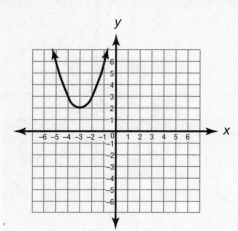

H

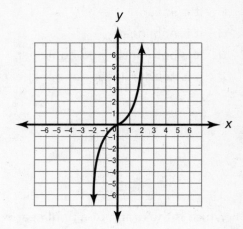

G

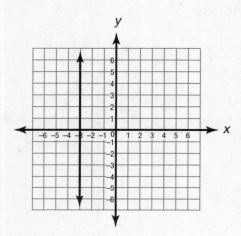

J

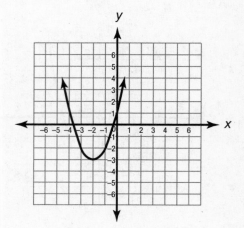

7   Which equation is not linear? (Hint: think about the graph of each equation.)

A $y = 4x$

B $y = 4x - 4$

C $y = 4x^2$

D $y = 4 - x$

8   Which term of the equation $y = 4x^2 + 2x - 20$ would you eliminate to create a linear equation? Write the term.

Answer _____

9 What word or words best describe the graph of a linear equation?

Answer _____

Short-Response Question

10 This graph shows the relationship between Fahrenheit and Celsius temperature.

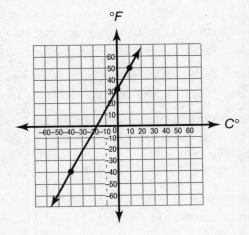

The equation used to make the graph is $F = 1.8C + 32$, where C represents Celsius temperature and F represents the corresponding Fahrenheit temperature.

Is the equation used to make this graph linear or nonlinear? Explain your answer.

_____

_____

_____

_____

LESSON 37

Strand 3: Geometry

Solving Systems of Two Linear Equations

8.G.18 Solve systems of equations graphically (only linear, integral solutions, $y = mx + b$ format, no vertical/horizontal lines)

A **system of linear equations** consists of two or more linear equations. The solution of a system of two linear equations consists of all solutions the two equations have in common. There are three possibilities for the solution:

- If the graphs of the two equations intersect, then the system has one solution—the coordinates of the point where the lines intersect.

- If the graphs of the two equations do not intersect—that is, they are parallel—then there is no solution to the system.

- If the graphs of the two equations are the same line, then all their solutions are in common and there are an infinite number of solutions to the system.

One way to solve a system of equations is to graph each equation and find the point of intersection of their graphs. You can save time graphing the lines by applying what you know about graphing lines in slope-intercept form, $y = mx + b$. See Lesson 35.

EXAMPLE

Solve the system of equations.

$y = x + 1$

$y = 2x - 3$

STRATEGY

Graph each equation and find the point of intersection.

STEP 1   Identify the slope and *y*-intercept for each equation.

In $y = x + 1$, the slope is 1 and the *y*-intercept is 1.

In $y = 2x - 3$, the slope is 2 and the *y*-intercept is -3.

STEP 2   Use the slope and intercept to graph each equation.

For $y = x + 1$:

Graph a point at (0,1) where the line crosses the *y*-axis.

From (0,1), count 1 unit up and 1 unit to the right to locate another point: (2,1).

Then draw a line through the two points.

For $y = 2x - 3$:

Graph a point at (0,-3) where the line crosses the *y*-axis.

From (0,-3), count up 2 units and 1 unit to the right to locate another point: (1,-1).

Then draw a line through the two points.

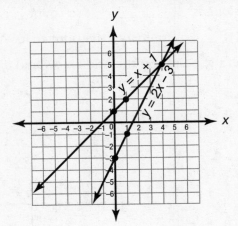

STEP 3   Find the point where the two lines intersect.

The lines intersect at the point with coordinates (4,5).

SOLUTION

The solution of the system is (4,5).

Note: You can also graph each equation by making a table of *x*- and *y*-values, graphing the ordered pairs, and drawing a line through the points.

What is the solution of this system of equations?

$y = x + 3$

$y = x - 3$

Let's check it out.

For the equation $y = x + 3$:

The *y*-intercept is _____.

The coordinates of the point where the line crosses the *y*-axis are

_____.

The slope is _____, so count _____ unit(s) up and

_____ unit(s) to the right to locate another point at _____.

Graph the points on the grid below and draw a line through them.

For the equation $y = x - 3$:

The *y*-intercept is _____.

The coordinates of the point where the line crosses the *y*-axis are

_____.

The slope is _____, so count _____ unit(s) up and

_____ unit(s) to the right to locate another point at _____.

Graph the points on the grid below and draw a line through them.

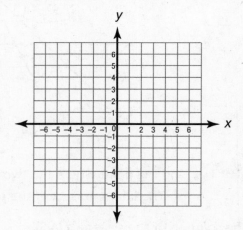

Do the lines intersect? _____

So, the system has _____ solution(s).

Sample Test Questions

1 What is the solution of the system of linear equations graphed below?

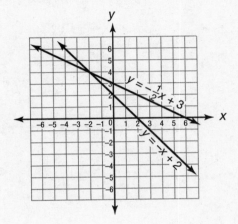

A (4, −2) C (0, 3)
B (0, 2) D (−2, 4)

2 What is the solution of the system of linear equations graphed below?

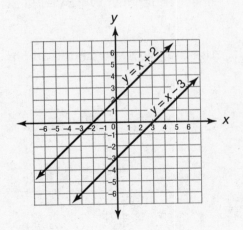

F all ordered pairs on both lines
G There is no solution.
H (0, 2)
J (0, −3)

3 Roland has to find the solution of this system of linear equations.

$$2y = 4x - 2$$

$$3y = 6x - 3$$

Without graphing, what is the solution? [Hint: Divide both sides of the first equation by 2, and divide both sides of the second equation by 3. Then compare the equations.]

A all ordered pairs on both lines
B There is no solution.
C (0, −2)
D (0, −3)

4 If two lines are parallel, what do you know about their equations?

F They have all their solutions in common.
G They have no solutions in common.
H They have exactly one solution in common.
J They have exactly two solutions in common.

5 What is the solution of the system of linear equations graphed below?

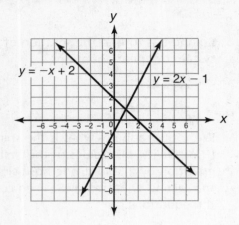

A $(2,-1)$

B $(2,2)$

C $(1,1)$

D $(1,2)$

6 What is the solution of the system of linear equations graphed below?

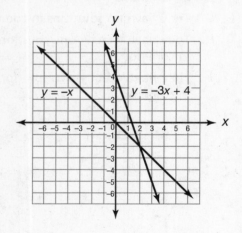

F $(2,-2)$

G $(-2,2)$

H $(2,2)$

J $(0,4)$

7 What is the solution of this system of linear equations?

$$y = x + 4$$

$$y = \frac{1}{3}x + 2$$

Use the grid to sketch the graphs.

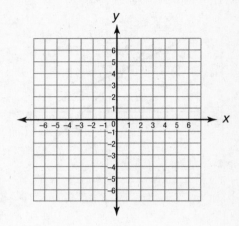

A $(-2,2)$ C $(-1,3)$

B $(-3,1)$ D $(4,2)$

8 What is the solution of this system of linear equations? Write your answer.

$$y = \frac{4}{3}x \qquad y = x + 1$$

Use the grid to sketch the graphs.

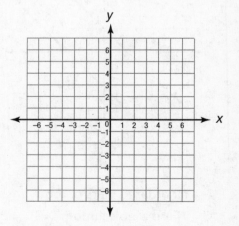

Answer _____

9   What is the solution of this system of linear equations? Write your answer.

$y = 3x + 2$

$y = x$

Use the grid to sketch the graphs.

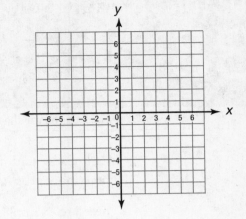

Answer _____

Short-Response Question

10

Part A

Graph this system of equations on the coordinate grid.

$y = \frac{1}{2}x + 4$

$y = \frac{1}{2}x - 3$

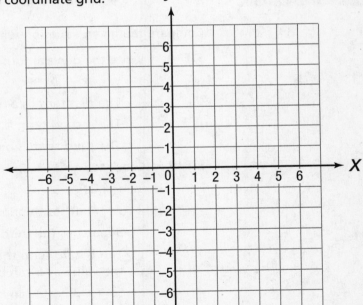

Part B

What is the solution of the system?

Answer _____

LESSON 38

Strand 3: Geometry

Recognizing Quadratics

8.G.21 Recognize the characteristics of quadratics in tables, graphs, equations, and situations

In a linear equation, the variable x is raised to the first power (x^1). The exponent is usually not written if it is 1.

These are examples of linear equations.

$$y = 2x \qquad y = -3x + 4 \qquad y = \frac{1}{2}x - 5$$

In a **quadratic equation**, the variable x is raised to the second power.

In general, a quadratic equation has this form:

$$y = ax^2 + bx + c$$

Where a, b, and c can be any numbers, but a cannot equal 0.

EXAMPLE 1

Is $y = 2x^2 - 3$ a quadratic equation?

STRATEGY

Compare the given equation with the general form for a quadratic equation.

STEP 1   Write the general form for a quadratic equation.

$y = ax^2 + bx + c$

The first term is a number a times x^2, or ax^2.

The second term is a number b times x, or bx.

The third term is a number c.

STEP 2   Check to see if $y = 2x^2 + 3$ matches the general form.

$y = 2x^2 + 3$

$2x^2$ matches the first term, ax^2, where $a = 2$.

3 matches the third term, c, where $c = 3$.

There is no term that matches the second term bx. However, the value of b can be 0.

So $y = 2x^2 + 3$ can be written as $y = 2x^2 + 0 \cdot x + 3$, where $a = 2$, $b = 0$, and $c = 3$.

SOLUTION

$y = 2x^2 + 3$ **is a quadratic equation.**

You can graph a quadratic equation by making a table of values to find ordered pairs. The ordered pairs can be connected with a curve called a **parabola**.

EXAMPLE 2

Draw the graph of $y = x^2 - 1$.

STRATEGY

Make a table of values for x and y. Graph the ordered pairs and connect them with a curve.

STEP 1   Make a table of values. This is another representation of the quadratic equation.

x	$y = x^2 - 1$	y	(x,y)
-2	$y = (-2)^2 - 1 = (-2 \times -2) - 1 = 4 - 1 = 3$	3	$(-2,3)$
-1	$y = (-1)^2 - 1 = (-1 \times -1) - 1 = 1 - 1 = 0$	0	$(-1,0)$
0	$y = (0)^2 - 1 = (0 \times 0) - 1 = 0 - 1 = -1$	-1	$(0,-1)$
1	$y = (1)^2 - 1 = (1 \times 1) - 1 = 1 - 1 = 0$	0	$(1,0)$
2	$y = (2)^2 - 1 = (2 \times 2) - 1 = 4 - 1 = 3$	3	$(2,3)$

STEP 2   Graph the points and connect them with a curve.

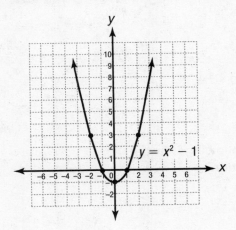

SOLUTION

Step 2 shows the graph of $y = x^2 - 1$.

Note the table in Step 1 of Example 2. The x- and y-values are not changing at a constant rate as they do in a table for a linear equation. Each x-value increases by 1, but the corresponding y-values decrease by 3, then decrease by 1, then increase by 1, and then increase by 3. Also note that the y-values go down and back up like a parabola.

Is $y = x^3 - 6$ a quadratic equation?

Let's check it out.

The general form of a quadratic equation is $y =$ _____ +

_____ + _____.

In the first term of a quadratic equation, the exponent of the variable x is

always _____.

In the first term of $y = x^3 - 6$, the exponent of the variable x is

_____.

So, $y = x^3 - 6$ is _____.

Sample Test Questions

1 Which of the following is a quadratic equation?

A $y = 4x^3 + 4x^2$

B $y = 4x - 4$

C $y = x^2 - 18x + 81$

D $y = x^4$

2 Which of the following is **not** a quadratic equation?

F $y = x^2 + 2$

G $y = x^4 + x^2$

H $y = 3x^2 - x - 2$

J $y = -x^2 + 4$

3 What are the values of a, b, and c in this quadratic equation?

$$y = -3x^2 + 2x - 6$$

A $a = 2; b = 2; c = 6$

B $a = 3; b = 2; c = 6$

C $a = -3; b = 2; c = 6$

D $a = -3; b = 2; c = -6$

4 Which of the following is the graph of $y = x^2 + 2$?

F

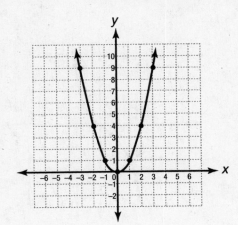

H

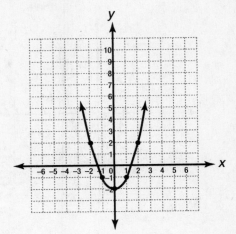

G

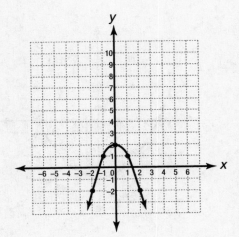

J

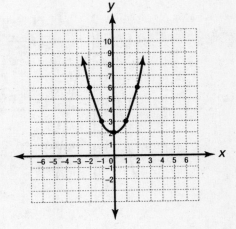

5 Which of the following is the graph of $y = -1x^2 + 5$?

A

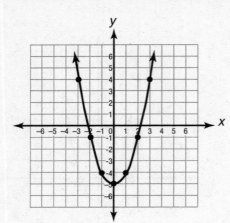

C

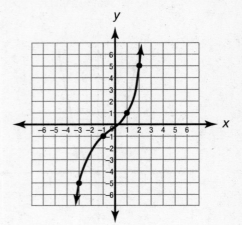

B

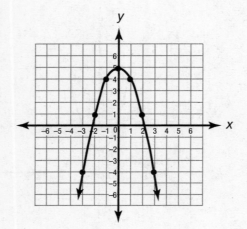

D

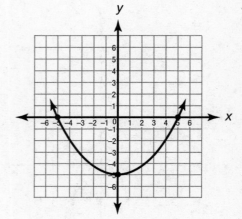

6 Which table of values matches this graph of a quadratic equation?

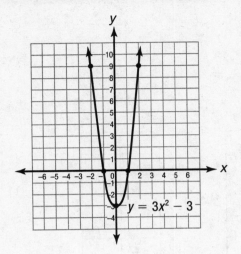

$y = 3x^2 - 3$

F

x	y
−2	9
−1	0
0	−3
1	0
2	9

H

x	y
−2	6
−1	3
0	0
1	3
2	6

G

x	y
−2	4
−1	1
0	0
1	1
2	4

J

x	y
−2	−8
−1	1
0	3
1	1
2	8

7 Which table shows values for a quadratic equation?

A

x	y
−2	5
−1	2
0	1
1	2
2	5

C

x	y
−2	−8
−1	−1
0	0
1	1
2	8

B

x	y
−2	2
−1	4
0	6
1	8
2	10

D

x	y
−2	4
−1	1
0	−2
1	−5
2	−8

8 Which is a linear equation?

F $y = 3x - 1$

G $y = x^2 + 5x - 4$

H $y = 6x^2$

J $y = x^3$

9 What must be true of an equation for it to be quadratic?

Answer _____

Extended-Response Question

10

Part A

Complete the tables of value for each equation.

$y = \frac{1}{2}x^2$

x	y
−4	
−2	
0	
2	
4	

$y = x^2$

x	y
−2	
−1	
0	
1	
2	

$y = 2x^2$

x	y
−2	
−1	
0	
1	
2	

Part B

Graph the three equations on this coordinate grid.

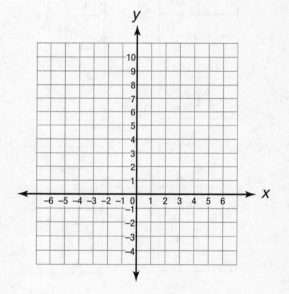

Part C

What are the numerical coefficients for each of the x^2 terms in each equation?

Answer _____

Part D

Explain how the numerical coefficient of the x^2 term affects the shape of the parabola.

_____

_____

_____

Progress Check for Lessons 29–38

1 Solve for x: $-5(x + 1) + 2x \leq 7$

A $x \leq 4$

B $x \leq -4$

C $x \geq 4$

D $x \geq -4$

2 What is the range of this relation?

$$\{(-2,1), (-1,0), (0,1), (1,2)\}$$

F $\{-2, -1, 0, 1\}$

G $\{0, 1, 2\}$

H $\{-2, -1, 1, 2\}$

J $\{4\}$

3 Which graph shows the solution of this inequality?

$$2x - 1 > -5$$

A

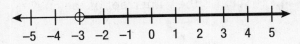

B

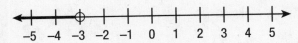

C

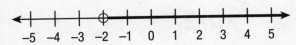

D

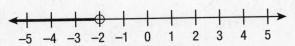

4 Which relation is a function?

F $\{(-2,0), (1,7), (-2,-2), (-3,-9)\}$

G $\{(0,1), (1,7), (2,17), (1,31)\}$

H $\{(-4,8), (-3,3), (1,3), (2,8)\}$

J $\{(0,4), (1,9), (-3,9), (0,14)\}$

5 This table represents the relationship of the number of hours (h) Shana worked and her total earnings (E).

h	E
1	33
2	51
3	69
4	87
5	105

Which equation represents the same relationship?

A $E = 15h + 18$

B $E = 18h + 15$

C $E = 10h + 23$

D $E = 33h$

6 Which table of values was used to graph this line?

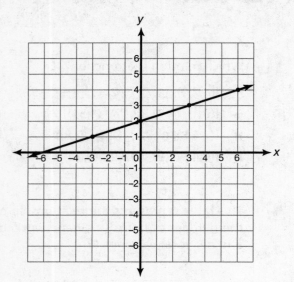

Use this graph for Questions 7 and 8.

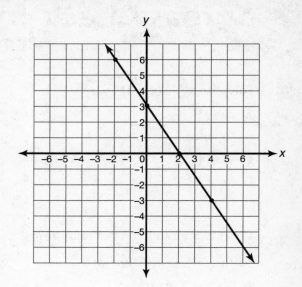

F

x	y
−3	0
0	1
3	3
6	4

H

x	y
1	−3
2	0
3	3
4	6

G

x	y
−3	1
0	2
3	3
6	4

J

x	y
−3	1
0	2
3	3
6	6

7 What is the slope of the line?

A $-\frac{3}{2}$

B $-\frac{2}{3}$

C $\frac{2}{3}$

D $\frac{3}{2}$

8 What is the y-intercept of the line?

F $\frac{2}{3}$

G $\frac{3}{2}$

H   2

J   3

9 A line has a slope of −3 and a *y*-intercept of 4. What is the equation of the line?

  A $y = 4x - 3$

  B $y = -4x + 3$

  C $y = -3x + 4$

  D $y = -3x - 4$

10 Which equation has this graph?

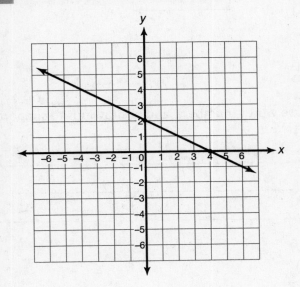

  F $y = -\frac{1}{2}x + 2$

  G $y = -\frac{1}{2}x + 4$

  H $y = \frac{1}{2}x + 2$

  J $y = \frac{1}{2}x + 4$

11 What construction does this drawing show?

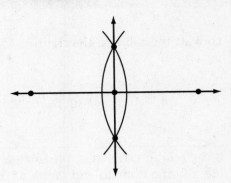

  A the bisector of an angle

  B an angle congruent to a given angle

  C the perpendicular bisector of a segment

  D a segment congruent to a given segment

12 Which equation is linear?

  F $y = x^2 + 1$

  G $y = x + 1$

  H $y = x^2 + x + 1$

  J $y = x(x + 2)$

13 Which equation is **not** quadratic?

  A $y = x^2 + 2x + 1$

  B $y = 2x^2 + 2x$

  C $y = 3x^3 + 2x^2$

  D $y = x(x + 5)$

Short-Response Questions

14   Look at the table to the right.

x	y
−3	7
−2	6
−2	5
1	4
3	3

Part A

Is the relation shown in the table a function?
Identify the domain and range of the relation.

Answer _____

Part B

Explain why your answer to Part A is correct. Use words, numbers, and/or drawings to support your answer.

_____

_____

_____

15   A line has slope of $\frac{1}{2}$ and a y-intercept of −2.

Part A

What is the equation of the line in slope-intercept form?

Answer _____

Part B

Draw a graph of the line on the axes to the right.

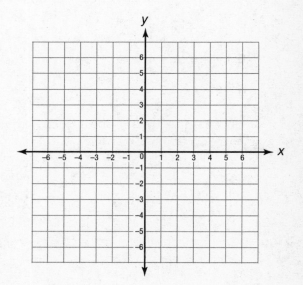

Extended-Response Questions

16

Part A

Construct the angle bisector of ∠C.

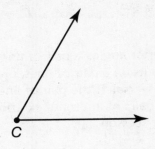

Part B

List the steps you took.

_____

_____

Part C

What does the angle bisector of an angle do?

_____

17

Part A

Graph this system of equations on the coordinate grid to the right.

$y = x + 3$

$y = -2x - 3$

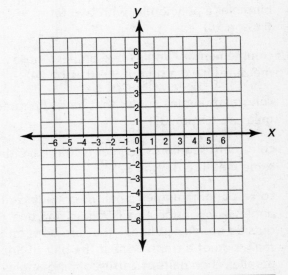

Part B

How many solutions does this system have? Explain your answer.

_____

_____

Part C

What is the solution of the system?

_____

Glossary

alternate exterior angles a pair of nonadjacent angles, both outside a pair of lines, on opposite sides of a transversal. If the pair of lines is parallel, then pairs of alternate exterior angles are congruent. (Lesson 25)

alternate interior angles a pair of nonadjacent angles, both inside a pair of lines, on opposite (alternate) sides of a transversal. If the pair of lines is parallel, then pairs of alternate interior angles are congruent. (Lesson 25)

adjacent angles angles that have a common side but no interior points in common (Lesson 24)

angle bisector a line, a ray, or a segment that divides an angle into two congruent angles (Lesson 32)

binomial a polynomial with two terms (Lesson 18)

complementary angles two angles whose measures have a sum of 90° (Lesson 24)

congruent angles angles that have the same measure (Lesson 32)

congruent segments segments that have the same measure (Lesson 32)

corresponding angles a pair of nonadjacent angles—one inside a pair of lines and one outside the pair of lines—that are both on the same side of a transversal. If the pair of lines is parallel, then pairs of corresponding angles are congruent. (Lesson 25)

dilation a transformation that expands or shrinks a figure to form a similar figure (Lesson 27)

domain the set of *x*-values in a relation consisting of ordered pairs (Lesson 30)

exponent a number used to show how many times another number, called a base, is used as a factor; these rules apply when working with exponents (Lesson 11)

FOIL method the name of a method for multiplying binomials

1. Multiply the **First** terms in the two binomials.

2. Multiply the **Outside** terms of the binomials; that is, multiply the first term of the first binomial by the second term of the second binomial.

3. Multiply the **Inside** terms of the binomials; that is, multiply the second term in the first binomial by the first term in the second binomial.

4. Multiply the **Last** terms in the two binomials.

5. If any of the products are like terms, combine them. (Lesson 20)

function a relation in which each domain value corresponds to one and only one range value; as ordered pairs, a set of ordered pairs such that no two ordered pairs have the same first value (Lesson 30)

inequality a mathematical sentence that uses a symbol, such as $<$, $\leq$, $>$, or $\geq$, to indicate that two quantities are not equal (Lesson 16)

interior angles on the same side of the transversal a pair of nonadjacent angles, both inside a pair of lines, on the same side of a transversal. If the pair of lines is parallel, then pairs of interior angles on the same side of the transversal are supplementary. (Lesson 25)

like terms terms that have the same variables raised to the same power (Lesson 18)

linear equation an equation whose graph is a straight line (Lesson 17)

monomial a number, a variable, or the product of a number and one or more variables (Lesson 18)

nonlinear equation an equation whose graph is not a straight line (Lesson 36)

order of operations A set of rules used to evaluate numerical expressions:

1. Do what is in parentheses first, starting with the innermost set;

2. Simplify all expressions with exponents;

3. Multiply and divide before you add and subtract;

4. Multiply in order from left to right;

5. Add and subtract in order from left to right. (Lesson 11)

ordered pair a pair of numbers, usually in the form (x,y), that can be graphed as a point on a coordinate plane (Lesson 17, 30)

parabola a curve that is the graph of a quadratic equation (Lesson 38)

parallel lines lines in the same plane that do not intersect (Lesson 25)

perpendicular bisector a line, ray, or segment that is perpendicular to a given segment and divides that segment into two congruent segments (Lesson 32)

percent the ratio of a number to 100 (Lesson 12)

polynomial a sum and/or difference of terms (Lesson 18)

quadratic equation an equation of the form $y = ax^2 + bx + c$, where a, b, and c can be any numbers and a is not zero (Lesson 38)

range the set of y-values in a relation consisting of ordered pairs (Lesson 30)

reflection a transformation that flips a figure (Lesson 26)

rotation a transformation that turns a figure around a point (Lesson 26)

similar figures figures that have the same shape, but not necessarily the same size; corresponding angles are congruent and corresponding side lengths are in proportion (Lesson 27)

slope the ratio of the vertical change in a line to the corresponding horizontal change; or the ratio of the rise to the run of a line (Lesson 33)

slope-intercept form of a linear equation a linear equation in the form $y = mx + b$, where m is the slope and b is the y-intercept (Lesson 35)

supplementary angles Two angles whose measures have a sum of 180° (Lesson 24)

system of linear equations two or more linear equations (Lesson 37)

term a number, a variable, or the product of a number and one or more variables (Lesson 18)

transformation a change in a figure's position or size (Lesson 26)

translation a transformation that slides a figure across a plane (Lesson 26)

transversal a line that intersects two or more other lines at different points (Lesson 25)

trinomial a polynomial with three terms (Lesson 18)

vertical angles two nonadjacent angles formed when two lines intersect; the angles in a vertical angle pair are congruent (Lesson 24)

y-intercept the y-coordinate of the point where a line crosses the y-axis (Lesson 34)

Punch-Out Tools

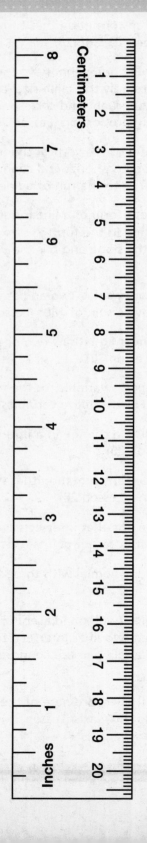

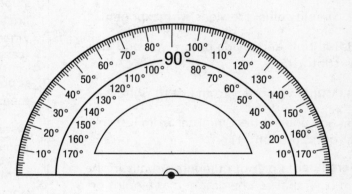

Notes

Notes

Notes

Notes

Notes

Notes

Notes

Notes

Notes

Notes

Notes

Notes